AUCASSIN AND NICOLETTE

AND OTHER MEDIAEVAL ROMANCES
AND LEGENDS

TRANSLATED, WITH AN INTRODUCTION,
BY EUGENE MASON

A Dutton **dep** *Paperback*

NEW YORK
E. P. DUTTON & CO., INC.

This paperback edition of
"Aucassin and Nicolette"
Published 1958 by E. P. Dutton & Co., Inc.

INTRODUCTION

THE tales brought together in this volume are drawn from the literature of the Middle Ages, and in many cases were written in France of the thirteenth century. I hope that they may be found interesting in themselves, but to appreciate them fully they should be considered in their relation to a definite historical background. Their conceptions of society, of religion, of politics, of humour are not common to all of us today. They are of the thirteenth century, and we are of the twentieth. To enjoy these tales without reserve it is necessary for a time to breathe the same air that was breathed—roughly speaking—by the subjects of St. Louis of France.

It is possible to love the period known as the Middle Ages, or it is possible to detest it. But you cannot ignore it, nor find it flavourless on the palate, because that period possesses character. Indeed, it is evident that the personal equation must largely determine what any writer's conception of the Middle Ages is. A great modern poet, for instance, loved the Middle Ages because economic conditions pressed less hardly on the poor; because London was small and white and clean; because chivalry afforded opportunity for that decorative treatment of knightly episodes which makes his poetry so attractive. Yet across the Channel, much at the same time, an equally distinguished poet treated of the same period in a book of poems which it is instructive to consider side by side with the work of

William Morris. The Frenchman's verse is lurid with fire and bigotry, and the tale of man's inhumanity to man. And the strange point is that both writers could give chapter and verse for the very different type of story they selected. Again, the religious temperament is apt to look back fondly to the Middle Ages as the "Age of Faith." To such minds mediaevalism is a period of easy acquiescence in spiritual authority, a state of health before the world grew sick with our modern disease of doubt. Certainly these centuries produced saints whose arresting examples and haunting words must always be the glory of Christianity, and it is equally certain that the offices and doctrines of the Church entered far more intimately into the lives of the common folk than they do to-day. But side by side with faith there was a "spirit of rebellion and revolt against the moral and religious ideas of the time." It may be found in many strangely different shapes: in the life of Abelard; in the extraordinary spread of witchcraft; and—in its supreme literary expression, perhaps—in a famous passage of "Aucassin and Nicolette." And, to take a third illustration of the same difficulty, were the Middle Ages years of sheer lyric beauty, or rather years of inexpressible ugliness and filth? "If you love the very words 'Middle Age'; if they conjure up to your mind glowing old folios of black letter with gilt and florid initials; crimson and green and blue pages in which slim ladies with spiked head-dresses walk amid sparse flowers and trees like bouquets, or where men-at-arms attack walled cities no bigger than themselves, or long-legged youths with tight waists and frizzed hair kiss girls under apple-trees; or a king is on a dais with gold lilies for his background, minstrels on their knees before him, lovers in the gallery"—well, if you accept all this dainty circumstance, you get sheer lyric beauty, and nothing else. Only there is another side, a side not very pleasant to dwell upon. Perhaps it would be truer to hold that the Middle Ages comprised all these things—the knight-errant and the tormentor; the altar and the witch's Sabbath; a dream of loveliness having its roots in slime and squalor. These centuries were both "enormous and delicate." They were great enough to include opposites, and to square the circle. You may love them, or you may hate them; but they cannot be ignored.

The philosophy of the Middle Ages—that is to say, the idea which governed their political and theological conceptions—was both simple and profound. The Emperor or King was considered to be the guardian of the temporal order of things, just as the Pope was held to be the supreme authority in matters of eternal and spiritual concern. It was an idea fascinating in its simplicity, but life is a tangled and complex matter, and in practice, planets, which in theory moved strictly in their own orbits, were continually striking across each other's path. Even St. Louis, the King, who carried saintliness to the extreme limit permitted to man, was involved in frequent political quarrels with the supreme head of his Church, and by one of the little ironies of fate came within measurable distance of excommunication. The King—again in theory—was the owner of all his realm. This was necessary to abolish Heptarchies. But for the support of the Crown he parcelled out his realm amongst great lords, and thus established Heptarchies again. The great barons, in their turn, divided their estates amongst knights, bound to assist them in their quarrels, and to furnish a certain number of soldiers to their service. Amongst these knights sprang up one of the supreme institutions of the Middle Ages—the institution of chivalry. "It took its birth in the interior of the feudal mansions, without any set purpose beyond that of declaring, first, the admission of the young man to the rank and occupation of the warrior; secondly, the tie which bound him to his feudal superior—his lord, who conferred upon him the arms of knighthood. But when once the feudal society had acquired some degree of stability and confidence, the usages, the feelings, the circumstances of every kind which attended the young man's admission among the vassal warriors, came under two influences, which soon gave them a fresh direction, and impressed them with a novel character. Religion and imagination, poetry and the Church, laid hold on chivalry, and used it as a powerful means of attaining the objects they had in view, of meeting the moral wants which it was their business to provide for." Throughout a long apprenticeship, in a castle which contained practically but one woman, the wife of his lord and she removed how infinitely from him in distance and in station, the young squire was trained to feel towards all women something of the dreamy devotion with which art and religion taught him to regard Our Lady herself. And the apprenticeship culminated in the ceremony of knighthood, with all the mystical significance of the symbolism preserved for us in the little story of Sir Hugh of Tabarie and the Sultan Saladin, carefully calculated to impress the recipient in the highest degree. Devotion to God, to his king, and to his lady—these were the ideals of knighthood, not always, unfortunately, its realities. But ideals are difficult of realization in so faulty a world as ours. The Black Prince was the very pattern of chivalry in his youth, yet Froissart remarks in his account of the battle of Poitiers that "the Prince of Wales, who was as courageous and cruel as a lion, took great pleasure this day in fighting and chasing his enemies." The conduct of that perfect gentle knight, Sir Graelent, towards the lady he discovered bathing in the fountain, was far from chivalrous, according to modern notions. Finally, here is a passage from a letter written by a knight of the fourteenth century to the Tyrant of Mantua, relating to a French girl, Jeannette, which is sufficiently explicit. "Let her be detained at my suit, for if you should have a thousand golden florins spent for her, I will pay them without delay, for if I should have to follow her to Avignon I will obtain this woman. Now, my lord, should I be asking a trifle contrary to law, yet ought you not to cross me in this, for some day I shall do more for you than a thousand united women could effect; and if there be need of me in a matter of greater import, you shall have for the asking a thousand spears at my back." Ah, well, ideals that are realized cease to be ideals.

Just as this worship of woman was the great social note of the Middle Ages, so the devotion to the Blessed Virgin was the distinguishing religious feature of those times. In honour of Our Lady were erected the magnificent Gothic cathedrals—those masterpieces of moral elevation—which stud the fair land of France like painted capitals upon a written page. In these build-

ings the genius of the Middle Ages found its supreme
expression. Above the crowded market-place and narrow mediaeval street rose those incomparable churches,
"like Gothic queens at prayer, alone, silent and
adorned." In her honour, too, they were made beautiful with glass and statuary, so that never before nor
since were churches filled with such an entrancing
congregation, never had buildings such wonderful
eyes. And at a time when masons built to her honour
and theologians defined her position, the story-tellers
were not slack in her praise. The three legends relating to the Virgin, which I have included in this book
of translations, are but specimens of an immense literature devoted to her service. "Our Lady's Tumbler"
is, to the modern taste, one of the most appealing of
all these legends, but there are others nearly, if not
quite, as beautiful. Once upon a time there was a
monk who was so ignorant that he was exposed to
the rebuke of his brethren. But in his devotion to Our
Lady he took for his meditation five psalms, each com-
mencing with a letter of her name. And when it
pleased God that his end should come, there happened
a very beauteous miracle, for from his mouth came
forth five fresh roses, sweet, crimson and leafy, in honour of the five letters of the name of Maria. Again,
how exquisite is the story of the nun who by frailty of
heart fled from her cloister to give herself over to sin.
After many long years she returned to the nunnery,
having lost her innocence, but not her faith, for during all her wanderings she had never omitted her habit
of prayer to Our Lady. But, to her surprise, always
she was addressed by her sisters as if she had never
gone from amongst them. For the Blessed Virgin, hav-

ing clothed herself with the vesture and seeming of the truant who loved her, even in sin, took also upon her the duties of a sacristan from which she had fled, so that no single person had noticed the absence from her cloister of the faithless nun.

Yet, after all, the Middle Ages delighted to honour Our Lady as the tender Mother rather than as the Queen of Heaven. In numberless miniatures, and on the portals of the cathedrals raised to her glory, she stands presenting her Child to the adoration of men. It is as the instrument of the Incarnation that her ultimate dignity consists. Indeed, the religion of the Middle Ages can only be appreciated by regarding it in the light of the doctrine of the Incarnation. Christ is God. The Mass—the popular service instituted by Himself—is an extension of His Incarnation. The Blessed Virgin is to be held in peculiar veneration as the Mother of God. The two threads can easily be seen twined together in that story of how Our Lady tourneyed whilst the knight was at Mass. But belief in the Incarnation is the keystone of mediaeval theology, and the only explanation of the lives of those saints who poured out their years like water in the service of God and man.

The authors of the stories brought together in this book from various sources are, in some cases, identified, but in others are unknown. They may, perhaps, be regarded as representative of the three classes who are responsible for this kind of fiction—the monk, the trouvére and the professional minstrel. The monk, for his part, wrote in French seldom enough. He was a scholar, and when he had something to say, preferred to deliver himself in Latin, the language common to all educated men. But, for once, in the thirteenth century, a monk of Soissons, named Gautier de Coinci, translated into French verse a great collection of the miracles of Our Lady. From this garner I have selected the legend "Of a Jew who took as Surety the Image of Our Lady." Gautier de Coinci may not have been a supreme poet—that saving grace comes seldom enough—but his industry was certainly abnormal. His labour of love must have been the occupation of a lifetime, and it is pleasant to recall the old monk, in silent scriptorium and shady cloister, turning the Latin legends into fluent and pious verse.

The trouvére was drawn from the same class as the troubadour, and the circumstances of their lives were in essentials much the same. He lived very probably in some nobleman's castle, where he composed his stories as a sort of amateur, and recited the verses to an audience more or less select. His pride forbade him to appear personally before the populace, but it permitted him to provide wandering minstrels with copies of these poems, and so entertain the common folk by deputy. In the lord's castle it was, of course, another matter. On summer afternoons he would recite before the baron's household, where they were seated on the steps of the garden terrace, each in his order and degree. You can feel the hush and heat of the Provençal evening, whilst the sombre cypresses spire into the sky, and the olives whisper, and, far below, the broad stretches of the Rhône are suffused with the lovely light and colour of southern France. Or, in winter, after supper, when the tables were cleared, the trouvére would recite in hall. At the feet of the ladies sat their knights on silken cushions, fettered with silver chains, each to his friend. It was an audience rich and idle, familiar with the fantastic lives of the trouba-dours, and with the wanton judgments of the Courts of Love. For such a company no flower of sentiment could be too highly scented, and no tale come amiss, save only that it spoke of love.

If the trouvéres were "the aristocracy of this litera-ture," the minstrel was its "democracy." Sometimes he rose almost to the status of the trouvére, composing his own stories, and reciting them even in kings' houses. Generally, however, the minstrel was but a strolling player, speaking other men's thoughts, and wandering over the length and breadth of the land. Occasionally he went alone with his viol. At other times he was accompanied by bears, or a little troupe of singing boys or dancing girls. The minstrel might have the good fortune to give his entertainment before some knight or count. At any rate, the common folk heard him gladly, before the church or on the village green. If he was lucky, the homeless minstrel got free lodgings for the night at some hospitable monastery, but occasionally he was turned from the door, with hard words, because of St. Bernard's saying that "the tricks of the jongleurs can never please God." Once upon a time such a minstrel as this knocked at a mon-astery door, and asked for hospitality. He was received without indecent joy, and the guest-master, forgetting that a grace conferred unwillingly is no favour at all, provided the guest with black bread, salted vegetables, cold water, and a hard and dirty pallet. The abbot obviously felt no passion for strolling vagabonds, and had appointed a guest-master after his own heart. On the morrow, when the minstrel was leaving the mon-

astery, he met the abbot returning from a short journey. To revenge himself, at any rate, on one of the
two, the minstrel accosted him effusively. "My lord,"
said he, "I thank you and all the community from the
bottom of my heart, for Brother such-an-one has welcomed me like Christ Himself last night. He lighted
a fire in my chamber, and served me with choice wines,
excellent fish, and more dishes than I am able to recall. And this morning when he bade me farewell he
gave me shoes, and these leathern laces, and a knife."
When the abbot heard this he was filled with anger,
and, parting shortly from the minstrel, he hastened to
the monastery, and promptly relieved the guest-master
of his office, before the latter could offer a word of
explanation. Thus was the minstrel revenged on this
grudging heart.

If, however, any reader would like to see closer the
actual life of a minstrel of the thirteenth century, I
would suggest that he obtain the excellent little book
on Rutebeuf, one of the most famous of them all,
published in the *Grands Écrivains Français* series.
There he may read of the poet's bare cupboard, and
the unfurnished lodging, where he lived with his ugly
and dowerless old wife, who brought him but fifty
years with her soup. He coughs with cold and gapes
with hunger. He has no mattress, but only straw, and
a bed of straw is not a bed. He fears to face his wife
without money for food and rent. If he cannot dig,
emphatically, to beg he is not ashamed. All his goods
are in pawn, and his time is wasted in the tavern,
playing dice, which are his curse and his downfall.
Well, Rutebeuf is not the first nor the last to be
ruined by dice. How the Devil must smile! Do you

remember the legend of the making of these little figures? A merchant who sold himself to the Devil was
bidden by him to make a six-sided piece of bone, and
to mark each side with a number. One point was to
insult the only true God. Two points were to insult
God and the Blessed Virgin. Three points to insult
the Holy Trinity. Four points to insult the four Evan-
gelists. Five points to insult the Sacred Wounds; and
six points to insult the Days of Creation. From that
hour the little figures spread rapidly through the
world, to man's confusion. Such is the picture Rutebeuf paints of his life—a life curiously anticipative of
that of many a Bohemian poet since. It is not a very
attractive picture, and though for artistic and other
reasons the shadows may be unduly darkened, yet in
the main it is doubtless substantially correct.

The stories written by such men as these are racy of
their soil, and give the very form and pressure of their
times. I have tried to make my selection representative, and have included in this book not only ro-
mances of love and chivalry, but legends of devotion
and moralities. Greatly daring, I have translated a
specimen of their humour even—not too characteris-
tic, I hope, of the robust merriment of the feudal
period. These stories will be found illustrative of some
of the ideas with which the mind of the Middle Ages
was concerned. The devotion to the Blessed Sacrament and to Our Lady; the languid and overwrought
sentiment of love; the mystical ceremonies of knighthood; all these things are illuminated by the tales
which follow this Introduction. Bound up with them
are customs and ideas which to the modern mind are,
perhaps, less happy. It seems odd, for instance, that

the feudal knight should see nothing repugnant in accepting money and clothing from the lady who had given him already the supreme favour of her love. It is possible to entertain a high ideal of friendship without being prepared to cut the throats of your children for the sake of your friend. Yet this is what Amile did for Amis in the great epic of friendship of the Middle Ages. In its stark adherence to a superhuman standard, it puts one in mind of the animal-like patience of Griselda—which story (not included here) may perhaps be regarded as the modest ideal of the mediaeval husband. It is strange, too, to find in stories so concerned with the knightly exercises of the tourney and the joust, no hint of the singular disfavour in which these games (or, perhaps, pursuits) were held by the Church. Popes prohibited them; St. Louis forbade them. Those slain therein were refused burial in consecrated ground. The Church testified, "Of those who fell in tournament there is no question but that they go down to hell, unless they are aided by the great benefit of absolution." At Cologne sixty knights and squires were killed, and the cries were heard all about of demons carrying off their souls to perdition. Apparently all this tremendous machinery failed utterly in its purpose. The most pious knights strove in tournaments equally with the most reckless, and—according to Miss Knox, to whose admirable *Court of a Saint* I am indebted—a son of St. Louis himself was thrown at a tourney, and was afterwards weak in intellect as a consequence.

Nor is it only with the lives of the rich that the mediaeval minstrel was concerned. He dealt, too, with the lives and aspirations of that yet more numerous

class, the poor. Such a story as "The Three Thieves"
is indeed a picture of the home of the hind. We see
the mean mud and timber hovel, into which the
thieves broke so easily, with its cauldron upon the fire
of fagots, its big bedstead, and the little lean-to byre.
The peasant's tools stood around the wall, whilst outside was the garden, in which a wise ordinance of St.
Louis required that pot-herbs should be planted. And
if the tale of "The Three Thieves" shows us the
home of the peasant, his soul is stripped for us to the
quick, in—of all places in the world of literature—
"Aucassin and Nicolette." Amongst the full-blown
flowers of sentiment in that incomparable love-story
is placed an episode which, in its violence and harsh
realism, has been likened to a spot of blood and mud
on a silver ground. Possibly it was inserted merely to
show the hero's good heart, or is simply an instance
of that artistic use of contrast so noticeable throughout the book. Anyway, there are few things in feudal
literature more striking than the meeting of the "dansellon" with the tattered, hideous ploughman, the one
weeping in delicate grief, the other telling, dry-eyed,
the sordid story of the abject poor. It is very far from
being the happiest incident in the romance, but it is
certainly one of the most memorable. One wonders
how it was taken by an audience that concerned itself
so little with the interests of the serf, and whose literature never mentioned that class, except in scorn. Was
the author possibly of the ploughman's kindred, like
Chaucer's parish priest in *The Canterbury Tales*? Had
the stinging whips of captivity taught him sympathy
with unpoetical sorrows; or is this an early hint of the
coming storm? "They are clothed in velvet, and warm

in their furs and their ermines, while we are covered with rags. They have wine and spices and fair bread; and we, oat-cake and straw, and water to drink. They have leisure and fine houses; we have pain and labour, the rain and the wind in the fields." We cannot tell; but comparing this dainty make-believe with that tragic misery, we feel the significance of the peasant's cry, "Woe to those who shall sorrow at the tears of such as these."

I hope I have not dwelt unduly on these stories considered as pictures of the customs and philosophy of their times. Perhaps, after all, these matters are of interest to the archaeologist and the ecclesiologist rather than to the general reader. Not being a scholar myself, I have no pretension to write for scholars. My object is more modest. I have tried to bring together a little garland for the pleasure of the amateurs of beautiful tales. To me these mediaeval stories are beautiful, and I have striven to decant them from one language into another with as little loss as may be. To this end I have refined a phrase, or, perhaps, softened an incident here and there. I do not pretend that they are perfect works of art. "All poets are unequal, except the bad, and they are uniformly bad." Sometimes a story drags, or there are wearisome repetitions. The psychology occasionally strikes a modern reader as remarkably summary. When Amis, for example, became a leper, we are gravely told that his wife held him in bitter hatred, and many a time strove to strangle him. Here is an author who, obviously, is astonished at nothing. But in reading these narratives you will remember how they have delighted, and been used by, writers in some cases greater than their own authors. Is it possible, for instance, to peruse "The Lay of the Little Bird" without recalling Shelley's "Sensitive Plant"? The tale of "The Divided Horsecloth" is told, in another version, both by Montaigne and Browning. The principal incident of "King Florus and the Fair Jehane" is used by Shakespeare in "Cymbeline." "Our Lady's Tumbler" and "A Jew Who Took as Surety the Images of Our Lady" have been re-written by Monsieur Anatole France with such perfection of art and artistry as to be the admiration and despair of all who come after him.

It should not be forgotten that the majority of these stories were intended to be recited, and not read. Repetition, therefore, is the more easily excused. This also accounts for the dramatic use of dialogue, so noticeable in "The Palfrey" and in "Aucassin and Nicolette." But it is evident that this Introduction will not permit me to go *seriatim* through these tales, "Item, a grey eye or so. Item, two lips, indifferent red." Let me therefore content myself with appreciating the most lovely of them all, "Aucassin and Nicolette."

A single copy of "Aucassin and Nicolette," transcribed in the thirteenth century, and preserved as by miracle, has retained for us not only a charming tale, but also a unique specimen of the minstrel's craft. Without it we could not have gathered that so elaborate a blending of prose and verse was possible to a strolling player of mediaeval France. The conte-fable was designed for recitation, with illustrative gesture, to the accompaniment of viol and pipes. In this, and not only in this, it seems to suggest an Eastern origin, and to-day, in any Moorish coffee-house, the tales of the *Arabian Nights* are delivered in a manner very similar to that witnessed in Provence seven hundred years ago. The peculiar quality of pleasure afforded by "Aucassin and Nicolette" is not to be found in the story itself. That, indeed, is very simple, and, perhaps, a trifle hackneyed. Aucassin, the only son of the Count of Beaucaire, is passionately in love with Nicolette, a beautiful girl of unknown parentage, bought of the Saracens, whom his father will not permit him to marry. The story turns on the adventures of these fond lovers, until at the end their common fidelity is rewarded. Portions have faded sadly, like old tapestry, and the laughter sounds especially hollow. But in "Aucassin" the part is emphatically greater than the whole, and its charm must rather be sought in its graceful turns of speech—jewels, five words long—and in the pictorial quality which makes it more a series of pictures than a narrative. Who can forget the still night of May on which Nicolette escapes from her prison, and hurries through the garden, kilting her skirt against the dew; or the ruined tower in whose kindly shadow she remains hidden, whilst the watch march along the moonlit street, their swords beneath their mantles; or that bower of branches, built by her own white hands, through the trellis-work of which her lover looks upon the stars! In such felicitous picture-making this classic is equalled by no work of its period.

EUGENE MASON

NOTE—The originals of these narratives are to be found in Romania; in the *Fabliaux et Contes des Po-*

étes François, edited by Barbazan et Méon; in two volumes of the *Nouvelles Françoises en Prose,* edited by Moland and D'Héricault; and in *Les Miracles de la Sainte Vierge,* by Gautier de Coinci.

CONTENTS

AUCASSIN AND NICOLETTE

'TIS OF AUCASSIN AND OF NICOLETTE

Who will deign to hear the song
Solace of a captive's wrong,
Telling how two children met,
Aucassin and Nicolette;
How by grievous pains distraught,
Noble deeds the varlet wrought
For his love, and her bright face!
Sweet my rhyme, and full of grace,
Fair my tale, and debonair.
He who lists—though full of care,
Sore astonied, much amazed,
All cast down, by men mispraised,
Sick in body, sick in soul,
Hearing shall be glad and whole,
    So sweet the tale.

Now they say and tell and relate:

How the Count Bougars of Valence made war on
Count Garin of Beaucaire, war so great, so wonderful,
and so mortal, that never dawned the day but that he
was at the gates and walls and barriers of the town,
with a hundred knights and ten thousand men-at-arms,
on foot and on horse. So he burned the Count's land,
and spoiled his heritage, and dealt death to his
men. The Count Garin of Beaucaire was full of years,
and frail; he had long outworn his day. He had no
heir, neither son nor daughter, save one only varlet,
and he was such as I will tell you. Aucassin was the
name of the lad. Fair he was, and pleasant to look

upon, tall and shapely of body in every whit of him. His hair was golden, and curled in little rings about his head; he had grey and dancing eyes, a clear, oval face, a nose high and comely, and he was so gracious in all good graces that nought in him was found to blame, but good alone. But Love, that high prince, so utterly had cast him down, that he cared not to become knight, neither to bear arms, nor to tilt at tourneys, nor yet to do aught that it became his name to do.

His father and his mother spake him thus—

"Son, don now thy mail, mount thy horse, keep thy land, and render aid to thy men. Should they see thee amongst them the better will the men-at-arms defend their bodies and their substance, thy fief and mine."

"Father," said Aucassin, "why speakest thou in such fashion to me? May God give me nothing of my desire if I become knight, or mount to horse, or thrust into the press to strike other or be smitten down, save only that thou give me Nicolette, my sweet friend, whom I love so well."

"Son," answered the father, "this may not be. Put Nicolette from mind. For Nicolette is but a captive maid, come hither from a far country, and the Viscount of this town bought her with money from the Saracens, and set her in this place. He hath nourished and baptized her, and held her at the font. On a near day he will give her to some young bachelor, who will gain her bread in all honour. With this what hast thou to do? Ask for a wife, and I will find thee the daughter of a king, or a count. Were he the richest man in France his daughter shalt thou have, if so thou wilt."

"Faith, my father," said Aucassin, "what honour of all this world would not Nicolette, my very sweet friend, most richly become! Were she Empress of Byzantium or of Allemaigne, or Queen of France or England, low enough would be her degree, so noble is she, so courteous and debonair, and gracious in all good graces."

Now is sung:

> Aucassin was of Beaucaire,
> Of the mighty castle there,
> But his heart was ever set
> On his fair friend, Nicolette.
> Small he heeds his father's blame,
> Or the harsh words of his dame.
>   "Fool, to weep the livelong day,
> Nicolette trips light and gay.
> Scouring she from far Carthage,
> Bought of Paynims for a wage.
> Since a wife beseems thee good
> Take a wife of wholesome blood."
> "Mother, naught for this I care,
> Nicolette is debonair;
> Slim the body, fair the face,
> Make my heart a lighted place;
> Love has set her as my peer,
>   Too sweet, my dear."

Now they say and tell and relate:

When the Count Garin of Beaucaire found that in nowise could he withdraw Aucassin his son from the love of Nicolette, he sought out the Viscount of the town, who was his man, and spake him thus—

"Sir Count, send Nicolette your god-child straightly from this place. Cursed be the land wherefrom she

was carried to this realm; for because of her I lose
Aucassin, who will not become knight, nor do aught
that it becometh knight to do. Know well that were
she once within my power I would hurry her to the
fire; and look well to yourself, for you stand in utmost
peril and fear."

"Sire," answered the Viscount, "this lies heavy upon
me, that ever Aucassin goes and comes seeking
speech with my ward. I have bought her with my
money, and nourished and baptized her, and held her
at the font. Moreover, I am fain to give her to some
young bachelor, who will gain her bread in all honour. With this Aucassin your son had nought to do.
But since this is your will and your pleasure, I will
send her to so far a country that nevermore shall he
see her with his eyes."

"Walk warily," replied the Count Garin, "for great
evil easily may fall to you of this."

So they went their ways.

Now the Viscount was a very rich man, and had
a rich palace standing within a garden. In a certain
chamber of an upper floor he set Nicolette in ward,
with an old woman to bear her company, and to
watch; and he put there bread and meat and wine and
all things for their need. Then he placed a seal upon
the door, so that none might enter in, nor issue forth,
save only that there was a window looking on the
garden, strict and close, whereby they breathed a little
fresh air.

Now is sung:

> Nicolette is prisoned fast,
> In a vaulted chamber cast,
> Shaped and carven wondrous well,

Painted as by miracle.
At the marble casement stayed
On her elbow leaned the maid;
Golden showed her golden hair,
Softly curved her eyebrows rare,
Fair her face, and brightly flushed,
Sweeter maiden never blushed.
In the garden from her room
She might watch the roses bloom,
Hear the birds make tender moan;
Then she knew herself alone.
" 'Lack, great pity 'tis to place
Maid in such an evil case.
Aucassin, my liege, my squire,
Friend, and dear, and heart's desire,
Since thou dost not hate me quite
Men have done me foul despite,
Sealed me in this vaulted room,
Thrust me to this bitter doom.
But by God, Our Lady's Son,
Soon will I from here begone,
   So it be won."

Now they say and tell and relate:

Nicolette was prisoned in the chamber, as you have heard and known. The hue and cry went through all the land that Nicolette was stolen away. Some said that she had fled the country, and some that the Count Garin of Beaucaire had done her to death. Whatever man may have rejoiced, Aucassin had no joy therein, so he sought out the Viscount of the town and spake him thus—

"Sir Viscount, what have you done with Nicolette, my very sweet friend, the thing that most I love in all the world? Have you borne her off, or hidden her from my sight? Be sure that should I die hereof, my blood will be required of you, as is most just, for I am slain of your two hands, since you steal from me the thing that most I love in all the world."

"Fair sire," answered the Viscount, "put this from mind. Nicolette is a captive maid whom I brought here from a far country. For her price I trafficked with the Saracens, and I have bred and baptized her, and held her at the font. I have nourished her duly, and on a day will give her to some young bachelor who will gain her bread in honourable fashion. With this you have nought to do; but only to wed the daughter of some count or king. Beyond this, what profit would you have, had you become her lover, and taken her to your bed? Little enough would be your gain therefrom, for your soul would lie tormented in Hell all the days of all time, so that to Paradise never should you win."

"In Paradise what have I to do? I care not to enter, but only to have Nicolette, my very sweet friend, whom I love so dearly well. For into Paradise go none but such people as I will tell you of. There go those aged priests, and those old cripples, and the maimed, who all day long and all night cough before the altars, and in the crypts beneath the churches; those who go in worn old mantles and old tattered habits; who are naked, and barefoot, and full of sores; who are dying of hunger and of thirst, of cold and of wretchedness. Such as these enter in Paradise, and with them have I nought to do. But in Hell will I go. For to Hell go the fair clerks and the fair knights who are slain in the tourney and the great wars, and the stout archer and

the loyal man. With them will I go. And there go the
fair and courteous ladies, who have friends, two or
three, together with their wedded lords. And there
pass the gold and the silver, the ermine and all rich
furs, harpers and minstrels, and the happy of the
world. With these will I go, so only that I have Nicolette, my very sweet friend, by my side."

"Truly," cried the Viscount, "you talk idly, for never
shall you see her more; yea, and if perchance you
spoke together, and your father heard thereof, he
would burn both me and her in one fire, and yourself
might well have every fear."

"This lies heavy upon me," answered Aucassin.

Thus he parted from the Viscount making great
sorrow.

Now is sung:

> Aucassin departed thus
> Sad at heart and dolorous;
> Gone is she his fairest friend,
> None may comfort give or mend,
> None by counsel make good end.
> To the palace turned he home,
> Climbed the stair, and sought his room.
> In the chamber all alone
> Bitterly he made his moan,
> Presently began to weep
> For the love he might not keep.
> "Nicolette, so gent, so sweet,
> Fair the faring of thy feet,
> Fair thy laughter, sweet thy speech,
> Fair our playing each with each,
> Fair thy clasping, fair thy kiss,
> Yet it endeth all in this.

> Since from me my love is ta'en
> I misdoubt that I am slain;
>   Sister, sweet friend."

Now they say and tell and relate:

Whilst Aucassin was in the chamber lamenting Nicolette, his friend, the count Bougars of Valence, wishful to end the war, pressed on his quarrel, and setting his pikemen and horsemen in array, drew near the castle to take it by storm. Then the cry arose, and the tumult; and the knights and the men-at-arms took their weapons, and hastened to the gates and the walls to defend the castle, and the burgesses climbed to the battlements, flinging quarrels and sharpened darts upon the foe. Whilst the siege was so loud and perilous the Count Garin of Beaucaire sought the chamber where Aucassin lay mourning, assotted upon Nicolette, his very sweet friend, whom he loved so well.

"Ha, son," cried he, "craven art thou and shamed, that seest thy best and fairest castle so hardly beset. Know well that if thou lose it thou art a naked man. Son, arm thyself lightly, mount to horse, keep thy land, aid thy men, hurtle into the press. Thou needest not to strike another, neither to be smitten down, but if they see thee amongst them, the better will they defend their goods and their bodies, thy land and mine. And thou art so stout and strong that very easily thou canst do this thing, as is but right."

"Father," answered Aucassin, "what sayest thou now? May God give me nought that I require of Him if I become knight, or mount to horse, or thrust into the press to strike knight or be smitten down, save only thou givest me Nicolette, my sweet friend, whom I love so well."

"Son," replied the father, "this can never be. Rather will I suffer to lose my heritage, and go bare of all, than that thou shouldest have her, either as woman or as dame."

So he turned without farewell. But when Aucassin saw him part he stayed him, saying—

"Father, come now, I will make a true bargain with thee."

"What bargain, fair son?"

"I will arm me, and thrust into the press on such bargain as this, that if God bring me again safe and sound, thou wilt let me look on Nicolette, my sweet friend, so long that I may have with her two words or three, and kiss her one only time."

"I pledge my word to this," said the father.

Of this covenant had Aucassin much joy.

Now is sung:

> Aucassin the more was fain
> Of the kiss he sought to gain,
> Rather than his coffers hold
> A hundred thousand marks of gold.
> At the call his squire drew near,
> Armed him fast in battle gear;
> Shirt and hauberk donned the lad,
> Laced the helmet on his head,
> Girt his golden-hilted sword,
> Came the war-horse at his word,
> Gripped the buckler and the lance,
> At the stirrups cast a glance;
> Then most brave from plume to heel

Pricked the charger with the steel,
Called to mind his absent dear,
Passed the gateway without fear
    Straight to the fight.

Now they say and tell and relate:

Aucassin was armed and horsed as you have heard. God! how bravely showed the shield about his neck, the helmet on his head, and the fringes of the baldric upon his left thigh. The lad was tall and strong, slender and comely to look upon, and the steed he bestrode was great and speedy, and fiercely had he charged clear of the gate. Now think not that he sought spoil of oxen and cattle, nor to smite others and himself escape. Nay, but of all this he took no heed. Another was with him, and he thought so dearly upon Nicolette, his fair friend, that the reins fell from his hand, and he struck never a blow. Then the charger, yet smarting from the spur, bore him into the battle, amidst the thickest of the foe, so that hands were laid upon him from every side, and he was made prisoner. Thus they spoiled him of shield and lance, and forthwith led him from the field a captive, questioning amongst themselves by what death he should be slain. When Aucassin marked their words,

"Ha, God," cried he, "sweet Creature, these are my mortal foes who lead me captive, and who soon will strike off my head; and when my head is smitten, never again may I have fair speech with Nicolette, my sweet friend, whom I hold so dear. Yet have I a good sword, and my horse is yet unblown. Now if I defend me not for her sake, may God keep her never, should she love me still."

The varlet was hardy and stout, and the charger he bestrode was right fierce. He plucked forth his sword, and smote suddenly on the right hand and on the left, cutting sheer through nasal and headpiece, gauntlet and arm, making such ruin around him as the wild boar deals when brought to bay by hounds in the wood; until he had struck down ten knights, and hurt seven more, and won clear of the *melée*, and rode back at utmost speed, sword in his hand.

The Count Bougars of Valence heard tell that his men were about to hang Aucassin, his foe, in shameful wise, so he hastened to the sight, and Aucassin passed him not by. His sword was yet in hand, and he struck the Count so fiercely upon the helm, that the headpiece was cleft and shattered upon the head. So bewildered was he by the stroke that he tumbled to the ground, and Aucassin stretched forth his hand, and took him, and led him captive by the nasal of the helmet, and delivered him to his father.

"Father," said Aucassin, "behold the foe who wrought such war and mischief upon you! Twenty years hath this war endured, and none was there to bring it to an end."

"Fair son," replied his father, "better are such deeds as these than foolish dreams."

"Father," returned Aucassin, "preach me no preachings; but carry out our bargain."

"Ha, what bargain, fair son?"

"How now, father, hast thou returned from the market? By my head, I will remember, whosoever may forget; so close is it to my heart. Didst thou not bargain with me when I armed me and fared into the press, that if God brought me again safe and sound, thou wouldst grant me sight of Nicolette, my sweet friend, so long that I might have with her two words or three, and kiss her once? Such was the bargain, so be thou honest dealer."

"I," cried the father, "God aid me never should I keep such terms. Were she here I would set her in the flames, and thou thyself might well have every fear."

"Is this the very end?" said Aucassin.

"So help me God," said his father; "yea."

"Certes," said Aucassin, "grey hairs go ill with a lying tongue."

"Count of Valence," said Aucassin, "thou art my prisoner?"

"Sire," answered the Count, "it is verily and truly so."

"Give me thy hand," said Aucassin.

"Sire, as you wish."

So each took the other's hand.

"Plight me thy faith," said Aucassin, "that so long as thou drawest breath, never shall pass a day but thou shalt deal with my father in shameful fashion, either in goods or person, if so thou canst!"

"Sire, for God's love make me not a jest, but name me a price for my ransom. Whether you ask gold or silver, steed or palfrey, pelt or fur, hawk or hound, it shall be paid."

"What!" said Aucassin; "art thou not my prisoner?"

"Truly, sire," said the Count Bougars.

"God aid me never," quoth Aucassin, "but I send thy head flying, save thou plight me such faith as I said."

"In God's name," cried he, "I plight such affiance as seems most meet to thee."

He pledged his troth, so Aucassin set him upon a horse, and brought him into a place of surety, himself riding by his side.

Now is sung:

> When Count Garin knew his son
> Aucassin still loved but one,
> That his heart was ever set
> Fondly on fond Nicolette;
> Straight a prison he hath found,
> Paved with marble, walled around,
> Where in vault beneath the earth
> Aucassin made little mirth,
> But with wailing filled his cell
> In such wise as now I tell.
> "Nicolette, white lily-flow'r,
> Sweetest lady found in bow'r;
> Sweet as grape that brimmeth up
> Sweetness in the spiced cup.
> On a day this chanced to you;
> Out of Limousin there drew
> One, a pilgrim, sore adread,
> Lay in pain upon his bed,
> Tossed, and took with fear his breath,
> Very dolent, near to death.
> Then you entered, pure and white,
> Softly to the sick man's sight,
> Raised the train that swept adown,
> Raised the ermine-bordered gown,
> Raised the smock, and bared to him
> Daintily each lovely limb.
> Then a wondrous thing befell,
> Straight he rose up sound and well,
> Left his bed, took cross in hand,
> Sought again his own dear land.
> Lily-flow'r, so white, so sweet,

Fair the faring of thy feet,
Fair thy laughter, fair thy speech,
Fair our playing each with each.
Sweet thy kisses, soft thy touch,
All must love thee over much.
'Tis for thee that I am thrown
In this vaulted cell alone;
'Tis for thee that I attend
Death, that comes to make an end,
    For thee, sweet friend."

Now they say and tell and relate:

Aucassin was set in prison as you have heard tell, and Nicolette for her part was shut in the chamber. It was in the time of summer heat, in the month of May, when the days are warm, long and clear, and the nights coy and serene. Nicolette lay one night sleepless on her bed, and watched the moon shine brightly through the casement, and listened to the nightingale plain in the garden. Then she bethought her of Aucassin, her friend, whom she loved so well. She called also to mind the Count Garin of Beaucaire, her mortal foe, and feared greatly to remain lest her hiding-place should be told to him, and she be put to death in some shameful fashion. She made certain that the old woman who held her in ward was sound asleep. So she rose, and wrapped herself in a very fair silk mantle, the best she had, and taking the sheets from her bed and the towels of her bath, knotted them together to make so long a rope as she was able, tied it about a pillar of the window, and slipped down into the garden. Then she took her skirt in both hands, the one before, and the other behind, and kilted her lightly against the dew which lay thickly upon the grass,

and so passed through the garden. Her hair was
golden, with little love-locks; her eyes blue and laughing; her face most dainty to see, with lips more vermeil
than ever was rose or cherry in the time of summer
heat; her teeth white and small; her breasts so firm
that they showed beneath her vesture like two round-
ed nuts; so frail was she about the girdle that your
two hands could have spanned her, and the daisies
that she brake with her feet in passing, showed altogether black against her instep and her flesh, so white
was the fair young maiden.

She came to the postern, and unbarring the gate,
issued forth upon the streets of Beaucaire, taking heed
to keep within the shadows, for the moon shone very
bright, and thus she fared until she chanced upon the
tower where her lover was prisoned. The tower was
buttressed with pieces of wood in many places, and
Nicolette hid herself amongst the pillars, wrapped
close in her mantle. She set her face to a crevice of
the tower, which was old and ruinous, and there she
heard Aucassin weeping within, making great sorrow
for the sweet friend whom he held so dear; and when
she had hearkened awhile she began to speak.

Now is sung:

> Nicolette, so bright of face,
> Leaned within this buttressed place,
> Heard her lover weep within,
> Marked the woe of Aucassin.
> Then in words her thought she told,
> "Aucassin, fond heart and bold,
> What avails thine heart should ache
> For a Paynim maiden's sake.
> Ne'er may she become thy mate,

Since we prove thy father's hate,
Since thy kinsfolk hate me too;
What for me is left to do?
Nothing, but to seek the strand,
Pass o'er sea to some far land."
Shore she then one golden tress,
 Thrust it in her love's duress;
Aucassin hath seen the gold
Shining bright in that dark hold,
Took the lock at her behest,
Kissed and placed it in his breast,
Then once more his eyes were wet
    For Nicolette.

Now they say and tell and relate:

When Aucassin heard Nicolette say that she would fare into another country, he was filled with anger.

"Fair sweet friend," said he, "this be far from thee, for then wouldst thou have slain me. And the first man who saw thee, if so he might, would take thee forthwith and carry thee to his bed, and make thee his leman. Be sure that if thou wert found in any man's bed, save it be mine, I should not need a dagger to pierce my heart and slay me. Certes, no; wait would I not for a knife; but on the first wall or the nearest stone would I cast myself, and beat out my brains altogether. Better to die so foul a death as this, than know thee to be in any man's bed, save mine."

"Aucassin," said she, "I doubt that thou lovest me less than thy words; and that my love is fonder than thine."

"Alack," cried Aucassin, "fair sweet friend, how can it be that thy love should be so great? Woman cannot love man, as man loves woman; for woman's love is in the glance of her eye, and the blossom of her breast and the tip of the toe of her foot; but the love of man is set deep in the hold of his heart, from whence it cannot be torn away."

Whilst Aucassin and Nicolette were thus at odds together, the town watch entered the street, bearing naked swords beneath their mantles, for Count Garin had charged them strictly, once she were taken, to put her to death. The warder from his post upon the tower marked their approach, and as they drew near heard them speaking of Nicolette, menacing her with death.

"God," said he, "it is great pity that so fair a damsel should be slain, and a rich alms should I give if I could warn her privily, and so she escape the snare; for of her death Aucassin, my liege, were dead already, and truly this were a piteous case."

Now is sung:

> Brave the warder, full of guile,
> Straight he sought some cunning wile;
> Sought and found a song betime,
> Raised this sweet and pleasant rhyme.
> "Lady of the loyal mind,
> Slender, gracious, very kind,
> Gleaming head and golden hair,
> Laughing lips and eyes of vair!
> Easy, Lady, 'tis to tell
> Two have speech who love full well.
> Yet in peril are they met,
> Set the snare, and spread the net.
> Lo, the hunters draw this way,
> Cloaked, with privy knives, to slay.
> Ere the huntsmen spie the chace
> Let the quarry haste apace
>   And keep her well."

Now they say and tell and relate.

"Ah," said Nicolette, "may the soul of thy father and of thy mother find sweetest rest, since in so fair and courteous a manner hast thou warned me. So God please, I will indeed keep myself close, and may He keep me too."

She drew the folds of her cloak about her, and crouched in the darkness of the pillars till the watch had passed beyond; then she bade farewell to Aücassin, and bent her steps to the castle wall. The wall was very ruinous, and mended with timber, so she climbed the fence, and went her way till she found herself between wall and moat. Gazing below, she saw that the fosse was very deep and perilous, and the maid had great fear.

"Ah, God," cried she, "sweet Creature, should I fall, my neck must be broken; and if I stay, tomorrow shall I be taken, and men will burn my body in a fire. Yet were it better to die, now, in this place, than to be made a show to-morrow in the market."

She crossed her brow, and let herself slide down into the moat, and when she reached the bottom, her fair feet and pretty hands, which had never learned that they could be hurt, were so bruised and wounded that the blood came from them in places a many; yet knew she neither ill nor dolour because of the mightiness of her fear. But if with pain she had entered in, still more it cost her to issue forth. She called to mind that it were death to tarry, and by chance found there a stake of sharpened wood, which those within the keep had flung forth in their defence of the tower. With this she cut herself a foothold, one step above the other, till with extreme labour she climbed forth from the moat. Now the forest lay but the distance of two bolts from a crossbow, and ran some thirty leagues in length and breadth; moreover, within were many wild beasts and serpents. She feared these greatly, lest they should do her a mischief; but presently she remembered that should men lay hands upon her, they would lead her back to the city to burn her at the fire.

Now is sung:

> Nicolette the fair, the fond,
> Climbed the fosse and won beyond;
> There she kneeled her, and implored
> Very help of Christ the Lord.
> "Father, King of majesty,
> Where to turn I know not, I.
> So, within the woodland gloom
> Wolf and boar and lion roam,
> Fearful things, with rav'ning maw,
> Rending tusk and tooth and claw.
> Yet, if all adread I stay,
> Men will come at break of day,
> Treat me to their heart's desire,
> Burn my body in the fire.
> But by God's dear majesty
> Such a death I will not die;
> Since I die, ah, better then
> Trust the boar than trust to men.
> Since all's evil, men and beast,
>   Choose I the least."

Now they say and tell and relate:

Nicolette made great sorrow in such manner as you have heard. She commended herself to God's keeping, and fared on until she entered the forest. She kept upon the fringes of the woodland, for dread of the wild beasts and reptiles; and hiding herself within some thick bush, sleep overtook her, and she slept fast until six hours of the morn, when shepherds and herdsmen come from the city to lead their flocks to pasture between the wood and the river. The shepherds sat by a clear, sweet spring, which bubbled forth on the outskirts of the greenwood, and spreading a cloak upon the grass, set bread thereon. Whilst they ate together, Nicolette awoke at the song of the birds and the laughter, and hastened to the well.

"Fair children," said she, "God have you in His keeping."

"God bless you also," answered one who was more fluent of tongue than his companions.

"Fair child," said she, "do you know Aucassin, the son of Count Garin of this realm?"

"Yes, we know him well."

"So God keep you, pretty boy," said she, "as you tell him that within this wood there is a fair quarry for his hunting; and if he may take her he would not part with one of her members for a hundred golden marks, nor for five hundred, nay, nor for aught that man can give."

Then looking upon her steadfastly, their hearts were troubled, the maid was so beautiful.

"Will I tell him?" cried he who was readier of word than his companions. "Woe to him who speaks of it ever, or tells Aucassin what you say. You speak not truth but faery, for in all this forest there is no beast—neither stag, nor lion, nor boar—one of whose legs would be worth two pence, or three at the very best, and you talk of five hundred marks of gold. Woe betide him who believes your story, or shall spread it abroad. You are a fay, and no fit company for such as us, so pass upon your road."

"Ah, fair child," answered she, "yet you will do as I pray. For this beast is the only medicine that may heal Aucassin of his hurt. And I have here five sous in my purse, take them, and give him my message. For within three days must he hunt this chace, and if within three days he find not the quarry, never may he cure him of his wound."

"By my faith," said he, "we will take the money, and if he comes this way we will give him your message, but certainly we will not go and look for him."

"As God pleases," answered she.

So she bade farewell to the shepherds, and went her way.

Now is sung:

> Nicolette as you heard tell
> Bade the shepherd lads farewell,
> Through deep woodlands warily
> Fared she 'neath the leafy tree;
> Till the grass-grown way she trod
> Brought her to a forest road,
> Whence, like fingers on a hand,
> Forked sev'n paths throughout the land.
> There she called to heart her love,
> There bethought her she would prove
> Whether true her lover's vows.
> Plucked she then young sapling boughs,
> Grasses, leaves that branches yield,
> Oak shoots, lilies of the field;
> Built a lodge with frond and flow'r,
> Fairest mason, fairest bow'r!
> Swore then by the truth of God

Should her lover come that road,
Nor for love of her who made
Dream a little in its shade,
'Spite his oath no true love, he,
    Nor fond heart, she.

Now they say and tell and relate:

Nicolette builded the lodge, as you have heard; very pretty it was and very dainty, and well furnished, both outside and in, with a tapestry of flowers and of leaves. Then she withdrew herself a little way from the bower, and hid within a thicket to spy what Aucassin would do. And the cry and the haro went through all the realm that Nicolette was lost. Some had it that she had stolen away, and others that Count Garin had done her to death. Whoever had joy thereof, Aucassin had little pleasure. His father, Count Garin, brought him out of his prison, and sent letters to the lords and ladies of those parts bidding them to a very rich feast, so that Aucassin, his son, might cease to dote. When the feast was at its merriest, Aucassin leaned against the musicians' gallery, sad and all discomforted. No laugh had he for any jest, since she, whom most he loved, was not amongst the ladies set in hall. A certain knight marked his grief, and coming presently to him, said—

"Aucassin, of such fever as yours I, too, have been sick. I can give you good counsel, if you are willing to listen."

"Sir knight," said Aucassin, "great thanks; good counsel, above all things, I would hear."

"Get to horse," said he; "take your pleasure in the woodland, amongst flowers and bracken, and the songs of the birds. Perchance, who knows? you may hear some word of which you will be glad."

"Sir knight," answered Aucassin, "great thanks; this I will do."

He left the hall privily, and went down-stairs to the stable where was his horse. He caused the charger to be saddled and bridled, then put foot in stirrup, mounted, and left the castle, riding till he entered the forest, and so by adventure came upon the well whereby the shepherd lads were sitting, and it was then about three hours after noon. They had spread a cloak upon the grass, and were eating their bread, with great mirth and jollity.

Now is sung:

> Round about the well were set
> Martin, Robin, Esmeret;
> Jolly shepherds, gaily met,
> Frulin, Jack and Aubriet.
> Laughed the one, "God keep in ward
> Aucassin, our brave young lord.
> Keep besides the damsel fair,
> Blue of eye and gold of hair,
> Gave us wherewithal to buy
> Cate and sheath knife presently,
> Horn and quarter staff and fruit,
> Shepherd's pipe and country flute;
>   God make him well."

Now they say and tell and relate:

When Aucassin marked the song of the herd-boys he called to heart Nicolette, his very sweet friend, whom he held so dear. He thought she must have passed that way, so he struck his horse with the spurs and came quickly to the shepherds.

"Fair children, God keep you."

"God bless you," replied he who was readier of tongue than his fellows.

"Fair children," said he, "tell over again the song that you told but now."

"We will not tell it," answered he who was more fluent of speech than the others; "sorrow be his who sings it to you, fair sir."

"Fair children," returned Aucassin, "do you not know me?"

"Oh yes, we know well that you are Aucassin, our young lord; but we are not your men; we belong to the Count."

"Fair children, sing me the song once more, I pray you!"

"By the Wounded Heart, what fine words! Why should I sing for you, if I have no wish to do so? Why, the richest man in all the land—saving the presence of Count Garin—would not dare to drive my sheep and oxen and cows from out his wheatfield or his pasture, for fear of losing his eyes. Wherefore, then, should I sing for you, if I have no wish to do so?"

"God keep you, fair children; yet you will do this thing for me. Take these ten sous that I have here in my purse."

"Sire, we will take the money; but I will not sing for you, since I have sworn not to do so; but I will tell it in plain prose, if such be your pleasure."

"As God pleases," answered Aucassin; "better the tale in prose than no story at all."

"Sire, we were in this glade between six and nine of the morn, and were breaking our bread by the well, just as we are doing now, when a girl came by, the loveliest thing in all the world, so fair that we doubted her a fay, and she brimmed our wood with light. She gave us money, and made a bargain with us that if you came here we would tell you that you must hunt in this forest, for in it is such a quarry that if you may take her you would not part with one of her members for five hundred silver marks, nor for aught that man can give. For in the quest is so sweet a salve that if you take her you shall be cured of your wound; and within three days must the chace be taken, for if she be not found by then, never will you see her more. Now go to your hunting if you will, and if you will not, let it go, for truly have I carried out my bargain with her."

"Fair children," cried Aucassin, "enough have you spoken, and may God set me on her track."

Now is sung:

> Aucassin's fond heart was moved
> When this hidden word he proved
> Sent him by the maid he loved.
> Straight his charger he bestrode,
> Bade farewell, and swiftly rode
> Deep within the forest dim,
> Saying o'er and o'er to him:
> "Nicolette, so sweet, so good,
> 'Tis for you I search this wood;
> Antlered stag nor boar I chase,
> Hot I follow on your trace.
> Slender shape and deep, blue eyes,
> Dainty laughter, low replies,
> Fledge the arrow in my heart.
> Ah, to find you, ne'er to part!
> Pray God give so fair an end,
>   Sister, sweet friend.

Now they say and tell and relate:

Aucassin rode through the wood in search of Nicolette, and the charger went right speedily. Do not think that the spines and thorns were pitiful to him. Truly it was not so; for his raiment was so torn that the least tattered of his garments could scarcely hold to his body, and the blood ran from his arms and legs and flanks in forty places, or at least in thirty, so that you could have followed after him by the blood which he left upon the grass. But he thought so fondly of Nicolette, his sweet friend, that he felt neither ill nor dolour. Thus all day long he searched the forest in this fashion, but might learn no news of her, and when it drew towards dusk he commenced to weep because he had heard nothing. He rode at adventure down an old grass-grown road, and looking before him saw a young man standing, such as I will tell you. Tall he was, and marvellously ugly and hideous. His head was big and blacker than smoked meat; the palm of your hand could easily have gone between his two eyes; he had very large cheeks and a monstrous flat nose with great nostrils; lips redder than uncooked flesh; teeth yellow and foul; he was shod with shoes and gaiters of bull's hide, bound about the leg with ropes to well above the knee; upon his back was a rough cloak; and he stood leaning on a huge club. Aucassin urged his steed towards him, but was all afeared when he saw him as he was.

"Fair brother, God keep you."

"God bless you too," said he.

"As God keeps you, what do you here?"

"What is that to you?" said he.

"Truly, naught," answered Aucassin. "I asked with no wish to do you wrong."

"And you, for what cause do you weep?" asked the other, "and make such heavy sorrow? Certainly, were I so rich a man as you are, not the whole world should make me shed a tear."

"Do you know me, then?" said Aucassin.

"Yes, well I know you to be Aucassin, the son of the Count, and if you will tell me why you weep, well, then I will tell you what I do here."

"Certes," said Aucassin, "I will tell you with all my heart. I came this morning to hunt in the forest, and with me a white greyhound, the swiftest in the whole world. I have lost him, and that is why I weep."

"Hear him," cried he, "by the Sacred Heart, and you make all this lamentation for a filthy dog! Sorrow be his who shall esteem you more. Why, there is not a man of substance in these parts who would not give you ten or fifteen or twenty hounds—if so your father wished—and be right glad to make you the gift. But for my part I have full reason to weep and cry aloud."

"And what is your grief, brother?"

"Sire, I will tell you. I was hired by a rich farmer to drive his plough, with a yoke of four oxen. Now three days ago, by great mischance, I lost the best of my bullocks, Roget, the very best ox in the plough. I have been looking for him ever since, and have neither eaten nor drunk for three days, since I dare not go back to the town, because men would put me into prison, as I have no money to pay for my loss. Of all the riches of the world I have nought but the rags upon my back. My poor old mother, too, who had nothing but one worn-out mattress, why, they have taken that from under her, and left her lying on the naked straw. That hurts me more than my own trouble. For money comes and money goes; if I have lost to-day, why, I may win to-morrow; and I will pay for my ox when pay I can. Not for this will I wring my hands. And you—you weep aloud for a filthy cur. Sorrow take him who shall esteem you more."

"Certes, thou art a true comforter, fair brother, and blessed may you be. What is the worth of your bullock?"

"Sire, the villein demands twenty sous for his ox. I cannot beat the price down by a single farthing."

"Hold out your hand," said Aucassin; "take these twenty sous which I have in my purse, and pay for your ox."

"Sire," answered the hind, "many thanks, and God grant you find that for which you seek."

So they parted from each other, and Aucassin rode upon his way. The night was beautiful and still, and so he fared along the forest path until he came to the seven cross-roads where Nicolette had builded her bower. Very pretty it was, and very dainty, and well furnished both outside and in, ceiling and floor, with arras and carpet of freshly plucked flowers; no sweeter habitation could man desire to see. When Aucassin came upon it he reined back his horse sharply, and the moonbeams fell within the lodge.

"Dear God," cried Aucassin, "here was Nicolette, my sweet friend, and this has she builded with her fair white hands. For the sweetness of the house and for love of her, now will I dismount, and here will I refresh me this night."

He withdrew his foot from the stirrup, and the

charger was tall and high. He dreamed so deeply on Nicolette, his very sweet friend, that he fell heavily upon a great stone, and his shoulder came from its socket. He knew himself to be grievously wounded, but he forced him to do all that he was able, and fastened his horse with the other hand to a thorn. Then he turned on his side, and crawled as best he might into the lodge. Looking through a crevice of the bower he saw the stars shining in the sky, and one brighter than all the others, so he began to repeat—

Now is sung:

> Little Star I gaze upon
> Sweetly drawing to the moon,
> In such golden haunt is set
> Love, and bright-haired Nicolette.
> God hath taken from our war
> Beauty, like a shining star.
> Ah, to reach her, though I fell
> From her Heaven to my Hell.
> Who were worthy such a thing,
> Were he emperor or king?
> Still you shine, oh, perfect Star,
>   Beyond, afar.

Now they say and tell and relate:

When Nicolette heard Aucassin speak these words she hastened to him from where she was hidden near by. She entered in the bower, and clasping her arms about his neck, kissed and embraced him straitly.

"Fair sweet friend, very glad am I to find you."

"And you, fair sweet friend, glad am I to meet."

So they kissed, and held each other fast, and their joy was lovely to see.

"Ah, sweet friend," cried Aucassin, "it was but now that I was in grievous pain with my shoulder, but since I hold you close I feel neither sorrow nor wound."

Nicolette searched his hurt, and perceived that the shoulder was out of joint. She handled it so deftly with her white hands, and used such skilful surgery, that by the grace of God (who loveth all true lovers) the shoulder came back to its place. Then she plucked flowers, and fresh grass and green leafage, and bound them tightly about the setting with the hem torn from her shift, and he was altogether healed.

"Aucassin," said she, "fair sweet friend, let us take thought together as to what must be done. If your father beats the wood to-morrow, and men take me, whatever may chance to you, certainly I shall be slain."

"Certes, fair sweet friend, the sorer grief would be mine. But so I may help, never shall you come to his hands."

So he mounted to horse, and setting his love before him, held her fast in his arms, kissing her as he rode, and thus they came forth to the open fields.

Now is sung:

> Aucassin, that loving squire,
> Dainty fair to heart's desire,
> Rode from out the forest dim
> Clasping her he loved to him.
> 'Laced upon the saddle bow
> There he kissed her, chin and brow,
> There embraced her, mouth and eyes.
> But she spake him, sweetly wise;
> "Love, a term to dalliance,
> Since for us no home in France
> Seek we Rome or far Byzance?"

"Sweet my love, all's one to me,
Dale or woodland, earth or sea;
Nothing care I where we ride
So I hold you at my side."
So, enlaced, the lovers went,
Skirting town and battlement,
Rocky scaur, and quiet lawn;
Till one morning, with the dawn,
Broke the cliffs down to the shore,
Loud they heard the surges roar,
    Stood by the sea.

Now they say and tell and relate:

Aucassin dismounted upon the sand, he and Nicolette together, as you have heard tell. He took his horse by the bridle, and his damsel by the hand, and walked along the beach. Soon they perceived a ship, belonging to merchants of those parts, sailing close by, so Aucassin made signs to the sailors, and presently they came to him. For a certain price they agreed to take them upon the ship, but when they had reached the open sea a great and marvellous storm broke upon the vessel, and drove them from land to land until they drew to a far-off country, and cast anchor in the port of the castle of Torelore. Then they asked to what realm they had fared, and men told them that it was the fief of the King of Torelore. Then inquired Aucassin what manner of man was this king, and whether there was any war, and men answered—

"Yes, a mighty war."

So Aucassin bade farewell to the merchants, and they commended him to God. He belted his sword about him, climbed to horse, taking his love before him on the saddle bow, and went his way till he came to the castle. He asked where the King might be found, and was told that he was in child-bed.

"Where, then, is his wife?"

And they answered that she was with the host, and had carried with her all the armed men of those parts. When Aucassin heard these things he marvelled very greatly. He came to the palace door and there dismounted, bidding Nicolette to hold the bridle. Then, making his sword ready, he climbed the palace stair, and searched until he came to the chamber where the King lay.

Now is sung:

> Hot from searching, Aucassin
> Found the room and entered in;
> There before the couch he stayed
> Where the King, alone, was laid,
> Marked the King, and marked the bed,
> Marked this lying-in, then said,
> "Fool, why doest thou this thing?"
> "I'm a mother," quoth the King:
> "When my month is gone at length,
> And I come to health and strength,
> Then shall I hear Mass once more
> As my fathers did before,
> Arm me lightly, take my lance,
> Set my foe a right fair dance,
>   Where horses prance."

Now they say and tell and relate:

When Aucassin heard the King speak thus he took the linen from the bed, and flung it about the chamber. He saw a staff in the corner, so he seized it, returned to the bed, and beat the King so rudely therewith, that he was near to die.

"Ha, fair sire," cried the King, "what do you require of me? Are you mad that you treat me thus in my own house?"

"By the Sacred Heart," said Aucassin, "bad son of a shameless mother, I will strike with the sword if you do not swear to me that man shall never lie in childbed in your realm again."

He plighted troth, and when he was thus pledged, "Sire," required Aucassin, "bring me now where your wife is with the host."

"Sire, willingly," said the King.

He got to horse, and Aucassin mounted his, leaving Nicolette at peace in the Queen's chamber. The King and Aucassin rode at adventure until they came to where the Queen was set, and they found that the battle was joined with roasted crab-apples and eggs and fresh cheeses. So Aucassin gazed upon the sight and marvelled greatly.

Now is sung:

> Aucassin hath drawn his rein,
> From the saddle stared amain,
> Marked the set and stricken field,
> Cheered the hearts that would not yield.
> They had carried to the fight
> Mushrooms, apples baked aright,
> And for arrows, if you please,
> Pelted each with good fresh cheese.
> He who muddied most the ford
> Bore the prize in that award.
> Aucassin, the brave, the true,
> Watched these deeds of derring do,
>   Laughed loudly too.

Now they say and tell and relate:

When Aucassin saw this strange sight he went to the King and asked of him—

"Sire, are these your foes?"

"Yea, sire," answered the King.

"And would you that I should avenge you on them?"

"Yea," answered he, "right willingly."

So Aucassin took sword in hand, and throwing himself in the *melée,* struck fiercely on the right and on the left, and slew many. When the King saw the death that Aucassin dealt he snatched at his bridle and cried—

"Hold, fair sire, deal not with them so cruelly."

"What," said Aucassin, "was it not your wish that I should avenge you on your enemies?"

"Sire," replied the King, "too ready is such payment as yours. It is not our custom, nor theirs, to fight a quarrel to the death."

Thereon the foemen fled the field.

The King and Aucassin returned in triumph to the castle of Torelore, and the men of the country persuaded the King that he should cast Aucassin forth from the realm, and give Nicolette to his son, for she seemed a fair woman of high lineage. When Nicolette heard thereof she had little comfort, so began to say—

Now is sung:

> Simple folk, and simple King,
> Deeming maid so slight a thing.
> When my lover finds me sweet,
> Sweetly shapen, brow to feet,
> Then know I such dalliance,
> No delight of harp, or dance,
> Sweetest tune, or fairest mirth.

All the play of all the earth
Seems aught of worth.

Now they say and tell and relate:

Aucassin abode in the castle of Torelore in ease and great delight, having with him Nicolette his sweet friend, whom he loved so well. Whilst his days passed in so easy and delightful a manner a great company of Saracens came in galleys oversea and beset the castle, and presently took it by storm. They gathered together the spoil, and bore off the townsfolk, both men and women, into captivity. Amongst these were seized Nicolette and Aucassin, and having bound Aucassin, both hands and feet, they flung him into one vessel, and bestowed Nicolette upon another. Thereafter a great tempest arose at sea, and drove these galleys apart. The ship whereon Aucassin lay bound, drifted idly, here and there, on wind and tide, till by chance she went ashore near by the castle of Beaucaire, and the men of that part hurrying to the wreck, found Aucassin, and knew him again. When the men of Beaucaire saw their lord they had much joy, for Aucassin had lived at the castle of Torelore in all ease for three full years, and his father and his mother were dead. They brought him to the castle of Beaucaire, and knelt before him; so held he his realm in peace.

Now is sung:

Aucassin hath gained Beaucaire,
Men have done him homage there;
Holds he now in peace his fief,
Castellan and count and chief.
Yet with heaviness and grief
Goeth he in that fair place,

> Lacking love and one sweet face;
> Grieving more for one bright head
> Than he mourneth for his dead.
> "Dearest love, and lady kind,
> Treasure I may never find,
> God hath never made that strand
> Far o'er sea or long by land,
> Where I would not seek such prize
>   And merchandize."

Now they say and tell and relate:

Now leave we Aucassin and let us tell of Nicolette. The ship which carried Nicolette belonged to the King of Carthage, and he was her father, and she had twelve brothers, all princes or kings in the land. When they saw the beauty of the girl, they made much of her, and bore her in great reverence, and questioned her straitly as to her degree, for certainly she seemed to them a very gracious lady and of high lineage. But she could not tell them aught thereof, for she was but a little child when men sold her into captivity. So the oarsmen rowed until the galley cast anchor beneath the city of Carthage, and when Nicolette gazed on the battlements and the country round about, she called to mind that there had she been cherished, and from thence borne away when but an unripe maid; yet she was not snatched away so young but that she could clearly remember that she was the daughter of the King of Carthage, and once was nourished in the city.

Now is sung:

> Nicolette, that maid demure,
> Set her foot on alien shore;

Marked the city fenced with walls,
Gazed on palaces and halls.
Then she sighed, "Ah, little worth
All the pomp of all the earth,
Since the daughter of a king,
Come of Sultan's blood, they bring
Stripped to market, as a slave.
Aucassin, true heart and brave,
Sweet thy love upon me steals,
Urges, clamours, pleads, appeals;
Would to God that peril past
In my arms I held you fast;
Would to God that in this place
We were stayed in one embrace,
Fell your kisses on my face,
   My dear, my fere."

Now they say and tell and relate:

When the King of Carthage heard Nicolette speak in this wise he put his arms about her neck.

"Fair sweet friend," said he, "tell me truly who you are, and be not esmayed of me."

"Sire," answered she, "truly am I daughter to the King of Carthage, and was stolen away when but a little child, full fifteen years ago."

When they heard her say this thing they were assured that her words were true, so they rejoiced greatly, and brought her to the palace in such pomp as became the daughter of a king. They sought to give her some king of those parts as husband and baron, but she had no care to marry. She stayed in the palace three or four days, and considered in her mind by what means she might flee and seek Aucassin. So she

obtained a viol, and learned to play thereon; and
when on a certain day they would have given her in
marriage to a rich king among the Paynim, she rose
at night and stole away secretly, wandering until she
came to the seaport, where she lodged with some poor
woman in a house near the shore. There, by means of
a herb, she stained her head and face, so that her fairness was all dark and discoloured; and having made
herself coat and mantle, shirt and hose, she equipped
her in the guise of a minstrel. Then, taking her viol,
she sought out a sailor, and persuaded him sweetly to
grant her a passage in his ship. They hoisted sail, and
voyaged over the rough seas until they came to the
land of Provence; and Nicolette set foot on shore, carrying her viol, and fared playing through the country,
until she came to the castle of Beaucaire, in the very
place where Aucassin was.

Now is sung:

> 'Neath the keep of strong Beaucaire
> On a day of summer fair,
> At his pleasure, Aucassin
> Sat with baron, friend and kin.
> Then upon the scent of flow'rs,
> Song of birds, and golden hours,
> Full of beauty, love, regret,
> Stole the dream of Nicolette,
> Came the tenderness of years;
> So he drew apart in tears.
> Then there entered to his eyes
> Nicolette, in minstrel guise,
> Touched the viol with the bow,
> Sang as I will let you know.
> "Lords and ladies, list to me,
> High and low, of what degree;

Now I sing, for your delight,
Aucassin, that loyal knight,
And his fond friend, Nicolette.
Such the love betwixt them set
When his kinsfolk sought her head
Fast he followed where she fled.
From their refuge in the keep
Paynims bore them o'er the deep.
Nought of him I know to end.
But for Nicolette, his friend,
Dear she is, desirable,
For her father loves her well;
Famous Carthage owns him king,
Where she has sweet cherishing.
Now, as lord he seeks for her,
Sultan, Caliph, proud Emir.
But the maid of these will none,
For she loves a dansellon,
Aucassin, who plighted troth.
Sworn has she some pretty oath
Ne'er shall she be wife or bride,
Never lie at baron's side
    Be he denied."

Now they say and tell and relate:

When Aucassin heard Nicolette sing in this fashion
he was glad at heart, so he drew her aside, and asked—

"Fair sweet friend," said Aucassin, "know you
naught of this Nicolette, whose ballad you have sung?"

"Sire, truly, yes; well I know her for the most loyal
of creatures, and as the most winning and modest of
maidens born. She is daughter to the King of Carthage, who took her when Aucassin also was taken,
and brought her to the city of Carthage, till he knew
for certain that she was his child, whereat he rejoiced

greatly. Any day he would give her for husband one of the highest kings in all Spain; but rather would she be hanged or burned than take him, however rich he be."

"Ah, fair sweet friend," cried the Count Aucassin, "if you would return to that country and persuade her to have speech with me here, I would give you of my riches more than you would dare to ask of me or to take. Know that for love of her I choose not to have a wife, however proud her race, but I stand and wait; for never will there be wife of mine if it be not her, and if I knew where to find her I should not need to grope blindly for her thus."

"Sire," answered she, "if you will do these things I will go and seek her for your sake, and for hers too; because to me she is very dear."

He pledged his word, and caused her to be given twenty pounds. So she bade him farewell, and he was weeping for the sweetness of Nicolette. And when she saw his tears—

"Sire," said she, "take it not so much to heart; in so short a space will I bring her to this town, and you shall see her with your eyes."

When Aucassin knew this he rejoiced greatly. So she parted from him, and fared in the town to the house of the Viscountess, for the Viscount, her god-father, was dead. There she lodged, and opened her mind fully to the lady on all the business; and the Viscountess recalled the past, and knew well that it was Nicolette whom she had cherished. So she caused the bath to be heated, and made her take her ease for fully eight days. Then Nicolette sought an herb that was called celandine, and washed herself therewith,

and became so fair as she had never been before. She
arrayed her in a rich silken gown from the lady's goodly store; and seated herself in the chamber on a rich
stuff of broidered sendal; then she whispered the
dame, and begged her to fetch Aucassin, her friend.
This she did. When she reached the palace, lo, Aucassin in tears, making great sorrow for the long tarrying of Nicolette, his friend; and the lady called to him,
and said—

"Aucassin, behave not so wildly; but come with me,
and I will show you that thing you love best in all the
world; for Nicolette, your sweet friend, is here from
a far country to seek her love."

So Aucassin was glad at heart.

Now is sung:

> When he learned that in Beaucaire
> Lodged his lady, sweet and fair,
> Aucassin arose, and came
> To her hostel, with the dame;
> Entered in, and passed straightway
> To the chamber where she lay.
> When she saw him, Nicolette
> Had such joy as never yet;
> Sprang she lightly to her feet
> Swiftly came with welcome meet.
> When he saw her, Aucassin
> Oped both arms, and drew her in,
> Clasped her close in fond embrace,
> Kissed her eyes and kissed her face.
> In such greeting sped the night,
> Till, at dawning of the light,
> Aucassin, with pomp most rare,
> Crowned her Countess of Beaucaire.
> Such delight these lovers met,

Aucassin and Nicolette.
Length of days and joy did win, .
Nicolette and Aucassin,
Endeth song and tale I tell
    With marriage bell.

THE STORY OF KING CONSTANT, THE EMPEROR

NOW telleth the tale that once upon a time there lived an Emperor of Byzantium, the which town is now called Constantinople, but in ancient days it was called Byzantium. In days long since there reigned in this city an Emperor; a Paynim he was, and was held to be a great clerk in the laws of his religion. He was learned in a science called astronomy, and knew the courses of the stars, the planets and the moon; moreover, in the stars he read many marvels; he had knowledge of many things which the Paynims study deeply, and had faith in divinations, and in the answers of the Evil One—that is to say, the Adversary. He knew, besides, much of enchantments and sorceries, as many a Paynim doth to this very day.

Now it chanced that the Emperor Muselin fared forth one night, he and a certain lord of his together, and went their ways about this city of Constantinople, and the moon shone very clear. They heard a Christian woman, travailing of child, cry aloud as they passed before her house; but the husband of this dame was set in the terrace upon his roof, and now he prayed God to deliver her from her peril, and again he prayed that she might not be delivered. When the Emperor had listened to his words for a long time, he said to the knight—

"Have you heard this caitif who prays now that his wife may not be delivered of her child, and again that she may be delivered? Surely he is viler than any thief, for every man should show pity to woman, and the greater pity to her in pain with child. But may Mahound and Termagaunt aid me never if I hang him not by the neck, so he give me not fair reason for this deed. Let us now go to him."

So they went, and the Emperor spake him thus, "Caitif, tell me truly why thou prayest thy God in this fashion, now that He should deliver thy wife in her labour, and again that she should not be delivered; this must I know!"

"Sire," answered he, "I will tell you readily. Truly I am a clerk, and know much of a science that men call astrology. I have learned, too, the courses of the stars and the planets, and thus I knew well that were my wife delivered in that hour when I prayed God to close her womb, then the child must be for ever lost, and certainly would he be hanged, or drowned, or set within the fire. But when I saw the hour was good, and the case fair, then I prayed God that she might be delivered; and I cried to Him, so that of His mercy He heard my prayer, and now the boy is born to a goodly heritage; blessed be God and praised be His Name."

"Now tell me," said the King, "to what fair heritage is this child born?"

"Sire," said he, "with all my heart. Know, sire, of a truth that the child born in this place shall have to wife the daughter of the Emperor of this town, she who was born but eight days since, and shall become Emperor and lord of this city, and of the whole world."

"Caitif," cried the Emperor, "never can it come to pass as thou sayest."

"Sire," answered he, "so shall it be seen, and thus behoveth it to be."

"Certes," said the Emperor, "great faith hath he who receives it."

Then they went from the house, but the Emperor commanded his knight that he should bear away the child in so privy a manner, if he were able, that none should see the deed. The knight came again to the house, and found two women in the chamber, diligently tending the mother in her bed, but the child was wrapt in linen clothes, and was laid upon a stool. Thereupon the knight entered the room, and set hands upon the child, and placed him on a certain table used for chess, and carried him to the Emperor, in so secret a fashion that neither nurse nor mother saw aught thereof. Then the Emperor struck the child with a knife, wounding him from the stomach to the navel, protesting to the knight that never should son of such a miscreant have his daughter to wife, nor come to sit upon his throne. He would even have plucked the heart from out the breast, but the knight dissuaded him, saying—

"Ah, sire, for the love of God, what is this thing that you would do! Such a deed becomes you naught, and if men heard thereof, great reproach would be yours. Enough have you done, for he is more than dead already. But if it be your pleasure to take further trouble in the matter, give him to me, and I will cast him in the sea."

"Yea,' cried the Emperor, "throw him in the water, for I hate him too much."

The knight took the child, wrapped him in a piece of broidered silk, and went with him towards the water. But on his way, pity came into his heart, and he thought within himself that never should new-born babe be drowned by him; so he set him, swathed in the silken cloth, on a warm muck-heap, before the gate of a certain abbey of monks, who at that hour were chanting matins. When the monks kept silence from their singing, they heard the crying of the child, and carried him to the Lord Abbot, who commanded that so fair a boy should be cherished of them. So they unswathed him from the piece of stuff, and saw the grisly wound upon his body. As soon, therefore, as it was day the Abbot sent for physicians, and inquired of them at what cost they would cure the child of his hurt; and they asked of him one hundred pieces of gold. But he answered that such a sum was beyond his means, and that the saving of the child would prove too costly. Then he made a bargain with the surgeons to heal the child of his wound for eighty golden pieces; and afterwards he brought him to the font, and caused him to be named Constant, because of his costing the abbey so great a sum to be made whole.

Whilst the doctors were about this business, the Abbot sought out a healthy nurse, in whose breast the infant lay till he was healed of his hurt, for his flesh was soft and tender, and the knife wound grew together quickly, but ever after on his body showed the gash. The child grew in stature, and to great beauty. When he was seven years old the Abbot put him to school, where he proved so fair a scholar that he passed all his class-mates in aptness and knowledge. When he was twelve years of age the boy had come to marvellous beauty; no fairer could you find in all the land; and when the Abbot saw how comely was the lad and how gracious, he caused him to ride in his train when he went abroad.

Now it chanced that the Abbot wished to complain to the Emperor of a certain wrong that his servants had done to the abbey. So the Abbot made ready a rich present, for the abbey and monastery were his vassals, although this Emperor was but a Saracen. When the Abbot had proffered his goodly gift, the Emperor appointed a time, three days thence, to inquire into the matter, when he would lie at a castle of his, some three miles out from the city of Byzantium. On the day fixed by the Emperor, the Abbot got to horse, with his chaplain, his squire, and his train; and amongst them rode Constant, so goodly in every whit that all men praised his exceeding beauty, and said amongst themselves that certainly he came of high peerage, and would rise to rank and wealth. Thus rode the Abbot towards the castle where the Emperor lay, and when they met, he greeted him and did him homage, and the Emperor bade him to enter within the castle, where he would speak with him of his wrong. The Abbot bowed before him and answered—

"Sire, as God wills."

The Abbot called Constant to him, for the lad carried the prelate's hat of felt, whilst he talked with the Emperor, and the Emperor gazed on the varlet, and saw him so comely and winning, that never before had he seen so fair a person. Then he asked who the boy was; and the Abbot answered that he knew little, save that he was his man, and that the abbey had nourished him from his birth—"and truly were this business of ours finished, I could relate fine marvels concerning him."

"Is this so?" said the Emperor; "come now with me to the castle, and there you shall tell me the truth."

The Emperor returned to the castle, and the Abbot was ever at his side, as one who had a heavy business, and he made the best bargain that he might, for the Emperor was his lord and suzerain. But the matter did not put from the Emperor's mind the great beauty of the lad, and he commanded the Abbot to bring the varlet before him. So the boy was sent for, and came with speed. When Constant stood in the presence, the Emperor praised his beauty, and said to the Abbot that it was a great pity that so fair a child should be a Christian. The Abbot replied that it was rather a great happiness, for one day he would render to God an unspotted soul. When the Emperor heard this thing he laughed at his folly, saying the laws of Christ were of nothing worth, and that hell was the portion of such as put faith in them. Sorely grieved was the Abbot when he heard the Paynim jest in this fashion, but he dared not to answer as he wished, and spake soft words to him right humbly.

"Sire, so it pleases the Almighty, such souls are not lost, for, with all sinners, they go to the mercy of the Merciful."

The Emperor inquired when the boy came to his hands, and the Abbot replied that fifteen years before he was found by night on the muck-heap before the abbey door.

"Our monks heard the wail of a tiny child as they came from chanting matins, so they searched for him, and carried him to me. I looked on the child, and he was very fair, so that I bade them to take him to the font and to cherish him duly. He was swathed in a rich stuff of scarlet silk, and when he was unwrapped I saw on his stomach a grievous wound; so I sent for doctors and surgeons, and bargained with them to cure him of his hurt for eighty pieces of gold. Afterwards we baptized him, and gave him the name of Coustant, because of his costing so great a sum to be made whole. Yet, though he be healed of his wound, never will his body lose the mark of that grisly gash."

When the Emperor heard this story he knew well that it was the child whom he had sought to slay in so felon a fashion; so he prayed the Abbot to give the lad to his charge. Then replied the Abbot that he would put the matter before his Chapter, but that for his own part the boy should be given to the King very willingly. Never a word, for good or evil, spake the King; so the Abbot took leave, and returned to the monastery, and calling a Chapter of his monks, told them that the Emperor demanded Constant from their hands.

"But I answered that I must speak to you to know your pleasure therein. Now answer if I have done aright."

"What, sire, done rightly!" cried the gravest and wisest of all the monks; "evilly and foolishly have you done in not giving him just what he asked at once. If you will hear our counsel, send Constant to him now as he requires, lest he be angry with us, for quickly can he do us much mischief."

Since it seemed to all the Chapter good that Constant should be sent to the Emperor, the Abbot bade the prior to go upon this errand, and he obeyed, saying, "As God pleases."

He got to horse, and Constant with him, and riding to the Emperor, greeted him in the name of the Abbot and the abbey; then taking Constant by the hand, gave him to the Emperor formally, in such names and in their stead. The Paynim received him as one angered that a nameless man and vagabond must have a king's daughter to wife, and well he thought in his heart to serve him some evil turn.

When the Emperor held Constant in his power, he pondered deeply how he might slay him, and no man speak a word. It chanced at this time that the Emperor had business which called him to the frontier of his realm, a very long way off, a full twelve days' journey. He set forth, carrying Constant in his train, yet brooding how to do him to death; and presently he caused letters to be written in this wise to the castellan of Byzantium.

"I, the Emperor of Byzantium, and lord of Greece, make him, the governor of my city, to know that as soon as he shall read this letter he shall slay, or cause to be slain, the bearer of this letter, forthwith upon the delivery thereof. As your proper body to you is dear, so fail not this command."

Such was the letter Constant carried, and little he knew that it was his death he held in hand. He took the warrant, which was closely sealed, and set out upon his way, riding in such manner that in less than fifteen days he reached Byzantium, the town we now call Constantinople. When the varlet rode through the gate it was the dinner-hour, so (by the will of God) he thought he would not carry his letter to table, but would wait till men had dined. He came with his horse to the palace garden, and the weather was very hot, for it was near to Midsummer Day. The pleasaunce was deep and beautiful, and the lad unbitted his horse, loosened the saddle, and let him graze; then he threw himself down beneath the shelter of a tree, and in that sweet and peaceful place presently fell sound asleep.

Now it happened that when the fair daughter of the Emperor had dined, she entered the garden, and with her four of her maidens, and soon they began to run one after the other, in such play as is the wont of damsels when alone. Playing thus, the fair daughter of the Emperor found herself beneath the tree where Constant lay sleeping, and he was flushed as any rose. When the Princess saw him, she would not willingly withdraw her eyes, saying to her own heart that never in her life had she beheld so comely a person. Then she called to her that one of her companions who was her closest friend, and made excuses to send the others forth from the garden. The fair maiden took her playfellow by the hand, and brought her towards the slumbering youth, saying—

"Sweet friend, here is rich and hidden treasure. Certes, never in all my days have I seen so gracious a person. He is the bearer of letters, and right willingly would I learn his news."

The two damsels came near the sleeping lad, and softly withdrew the letter. When the Princess read the warrant she began to weep very bitterly, and said to her companion, "Certainly this is a heavy matter."

"Ah, madame," said her fellow, "tell me all the case."

"Truly," answered the Princess, "could I but trust you fully, such heaviness should soon be turned to joy."

"Lady," replied she, "surely you may trust me; never will I make known that which you desire to be hid."

So that maiden, the daughter of the Emperor, caused her fellow to pledge faith by all that she held most dear, and then she revealed what the letter held; and the girl answered her—

"Lady, what would you do herein?"

"I will tell you readily," said the Princess. "I will put within his girdle another letter from my father in place of this, bidding the castellan to give me as wife to this comely youth, and to call all the people of this realm to the wedding banquet; for be sure that the youth is loyal and true, and a man of peerage."

When the maiden heard this she said within herself that such a turn were good to play.

"But, Lady, how may you get the seal of your father to the letter?"

"Very easily," answered the Princess; "ere my father left for the marches he gave me eight sheets of parchment, sealed at the foot with his seal, but with nothing written thereon, and there will I set all that I have told you."

"Lady," said she, "right wisely have you spoken; but lose no time, and hasten lest he awake."

"I will go now," said the Princess.

The fair maiden, the daughter of the Emperor, went straight to her wedding chest, and drew there-

from one of the sealed parchments left her by her
father, so that she might borrow moneys in his name
should occasion arise. For, always was this king and
his people at war with felon and mighty princes whose
frontiers were upon his borders. Thereon she wrote
her letter in such manner as this—

"I, King Muselin, Emperor of Greece and of Byzantium the great city, to my Castellan of Byzantium
greeting. I command you to give the bearer of this
letter to my fair daughter in marriage, according to
our holy law; for I have heard, and am well persuaded, that he is of noble descent and right worthy
the daughter of a king. And, moreover, at such time
grant holiday and proclaim high festival to all burgesses of the city, and throughout my realm."

In such fashion wrote and witnessed the letter of
that fair maiden the daughter of the Emperor. So
when her letter was finished she hastened to the garden, she and her playmate together, and finding Constant yet asleep, placed privily the letter beneath his
girdle. Then the two girls began to sing and to make
such stir as must needs arouse him. The lad awoke
from his slumber, and was all amazed at the beauty of
the lady and her companion. They drew near, and the
Princess gave him gracious greeting, whereupon Constant got to his feet and returned her salutation right
courteously. She inquired of him as to his name and
his business, and he answered that he was the bearer
of letters from the Emperor to the governor of the
city. The girl replied that she would bring him at once
to the presence of the castellan; so she took him by

the hand and led him within the palace; and all within the hall rose at the girl's approach, and did reverence to their Lady.

The demoiselle sought after the castellan, who was in his chamber, and there she brought the varlet, who held forth his letter, and added thereto the Emperor's greeting. The seneschal made much of the lad, kissing his hand; but the maid for her part kissed both letter and seal, as one moved with delight, for it was long since she had learned her father's news. Afterwards she said to the governor that it were well to read the dispatch in counsel together, and this she said innocently as one who knew nothing of what was therein. To this the castellan agreed, so he and the maiden passed to the council chamber alone. Thereupon the girl unfolded the letter, and made it known to the governor, and she seemed altogether amazed and distraught as she read. But the castellan took her to task.

"Lady, certainly the will of my lord your father must be done; otherwise will his blame come upon us with a heavy hand."

But the girl made answer to this—

"How, then, should I be married, and my lord and father far away? A strange thing this would be; and certainly will I not be wed."

"Ah, lady," cried the castellan, "what words are these? Your father's letter biddeth you to marry, so give not nay for yea."

"Sire," said the demoiselle, to whom time went heavy till all was done—"speak you to the lords and dignitaries of this realm, and take counsel together. So they deem that thus it must be, who am I to gainsay them?"

The castellan approved such modest and becoming words, so he took counsel with the barons, and showed them his letter, and all agreed that the letter must be obeyed, and the commandment of the Emperor done. Thus was wedded according to Paynim ritual Constant, that comely lad, to the fair daughter of the Emperor. The marriage feast lasted fifteen days, and all Byzantium kept holiday and high festival; no business was thought of in the city, save that of eating and drinking and making merry. This was all the work men did.

The Emperor tarried a long time in the borders of his land, but when his task was ended he returned towards Byzantium. Whilst he was about two days' journey from the city, there met him a messenger with letters of moment. The King inquired of him as to the news of the capital, and the messenger made answer that there men thought of nought else but drinking and eating and taking their ease, and had so done for a whole fortnight.

"Why is this?" asked the Emperor.

"Why, sire, do you not remember?"

"Truly, no," said the Emperor; "so tell me the reason."

"Sire," replied the varlet, "you sent to your castellan a certain comely lad, and he bore with him letters from you commanding that he should be wed to your daughter, the fair Princess, since after your death he would be Emperor in your stead, for he was a man of lineage, and well worthy so high a bride. But your daughter refused to marry such an one, till the castellan had spoken with the lords; so he showed the council your letter, and they all advised him to carry out

your will. When your daughter knew that they were
all of one mind, she dared no longer to withstand
you, and consented to your purpose. In just such manner as this was your daughter wedded, and a merrier
city than yours could no man wish to see."

When the Emperor heard this thing from the messenger, he marvelled beyond measure, and turned it
over in his thoughts; so presently he inquired of the
varlet how long it was since Constant had wedded his
daughter, and whether he had bedded with her.

"Yea, sire," answered the varlet, "and since it is
more than three weeks that they were married, perchance one day will she be mother as well as wife."

"Truly it were a happy hazard," said the Emperor,
"and since the thing has fallen thus, let me endure it
with a smiling face, for nothing else is left to do."

The Emperor went on his way until he reached
Byzantium, and all the city gave him loyal greeting.
Amongst those who came to meet him was the fair
Princess with her husband, Constant, so gracious in
person that no man was ever goodlier. The Emperor,
who was a wise prince, made much of both of them,
and laid his two hands on their two heads, and held
them so for long, for such is the fashion of blessing
amongst the Paynim. That night the Emperor considered this strange adventure, and how it must have
chanced, and so deeply did he think upon it that well
he knew that the game had been played him by his
daughter. He did not reproach her, but bade them
bring the letter he sent to the governor, and when it
was shown him he read the writing therein, and saw
that it was sealed with his very seal. So, seeing the
way in which the thing had come to pass, he said

within himself that he had striven against those things which were written in the stars.

After this the Emperor made Constant, his newly wedded son, a belted knight, and gave and delivered to him his whole realm in heritage after his death. Constant bore himself wisely and well, as became a good knight, bold and chivalrous, and defended the land right well against all its foes. In no long while his lord the Emperor died, and was laid in the grave, according to Paynim ritual, with great pomp and ceremony. The Emperor Constant reigned in his stead, and greatly he loved and honoured the Abbot who had cherished him, and he made him Chancellor of his kingdom. Then, by the advice of the Abbot, and according to the will of God, the All Powerful, the Emperor Constant brought his wife to the font, and caused all men of that realm to be converted to the law of Jesus Christ. He begot on his wife an heir, whom he christened Constantine, and who became true Christian and a very perfect knight. In his day was the city first called Constantinople, because of Constant his father, who cost the abbey so great a sum, but before then was the city known as Byzantium.

So endeth in this place the story of King Constant, the Emperor.

OUR LADY'S TUMBLER

AMONGST the lives of the ancient Fathers, wherein may be found much profitable matter, this story is told for a true ensample. I do not say that you may not often have heard a fairer story, but at least this is not to be despised, and is well worth the telling. Now therefore will I say and narrate what chanced to this minstrel.

He erred up and down, to and fro, so often and in so many places, that he took the whole world in despite, and sought rest in a certain Holy Order. Horses and raiment and money, yea, all that he had, he straightway put from him, and seeking shelter from the world, was firmly set never to put foot within it more. For this cause he took refuge in this Holy Order, amongst the monks of Clairvaux. Now, though this dancer was comely of face and shapely of person, yet when he had once entered the monastery he found that he was master of no craft practised therein. In the world he had gained his bread by tumbling and dancing and feats of address. To leap, to spring, such matters he knew well, but of greater things he knew nothing, for he had never spelled from book—nor Paternoster, nor canticle, nor creed, nor Hail Mary, nor aught concerning his soul's salvation.

When the minstrel had joined himself to the Order he marked how the tonsured monks spoke amongst themselves by signs, no words coming from their lips, so he thought within himself that they were dumb. But when he learned that truly it was by way of pen-

ance that speech was forbidden to their mouths, and
that for holy obedience were they silent, then considered he that silence became him also; and he refrained
his tongue from words, so discreetly and for so long a
space, that day in, day out, he spake never, save by
commandment; so that the cloister often rang with
the brothers' mirth. The tumbler moved amongst his
fellows like a man ashamed, for he had neither part
nor lot in all the business of the monastery, and for
this he was right sad and sorrowful. He saw the monks
and the penitents about him, each serving God, in
this place and that, according to his office and degree.
He marked the priests at their ritual before the altars; the deacons at the gospels; the sub-deacons at the
epistles; and the ministers about the vigils. This one
repeats the introit; this other the lesson; cantors chant
from the psalter; penitents spell out the Miserere—for
thus are all things sweetly ordered—yea, and the most
ignorant amongst them yet can pray his Paternoster.
Wherever he went, here or there, in office or cloister,
in every quiet corner and nook, there he found five,
or three, or two, or at least one. He gazes earnestly, if
so he is able, upon each. Such an one laments; this
other is in tears; yet another grieves and sighs. He
marvels at their sorrow. Then he said, "Holy Mary,
what bitter grief have all these men that they smite
the breast so grievously! Too sad of heart, meseems,
are they who make such bitter dole together. Ah, St.
Mary, alas, what words are these I say! These men are
calling on the mercy of God, but I—what do I here!
Here there is none so mean or vile but who serves
God in his office and degree, save only me, for I work
not, neither can I preach. Caitif and shamed was I

when I thrust myself herein, seeing that I can do nothing well, either in labour or in prayer. I see my brothers upon their errands, one behind the other; but I do naught but fill my belly with the meat that they provide. If they perceive this thing, certainly shall I be in an evil case, for they will cast me out amongst the dogs, and none will take pity on the glutton and the idle man. Truly am I a caitif, set in a high place for a sign." Then he wept for very woe, and would that he was quiet in the grave. "Mary, Mother," quoth he, "pray now your Heavenly Father that He keep me in His pleasure, and give me such good counsel that I may truly serve both Him and you; yea, and may deserve that meat which now is bitter in my mouth."

Driven mad with thoughts such as these, he wandered about the abbey until he found himself within the crypt, and took sanctuary by the altar, crouching close as he was able. Above the altar was carved the statue of Madame St. Mary. Truly his steps had not erred when he sought that refuge; nay, but rather, God who knows His own had led him thither by the hand. When he heard the bells ring for Mass he sprang to his feet all dismayed. "Ha!" said he; "now am I betrayed. Each adds his mite to the great offering, save only me. Like a tethered ox, naught I do but chew the cud, and waste good victuals on a useless man. Shall I speak my thought? Shall I work my will? By the Mother of God, thus am I set to do. None is here to blame. I will do that which I can, and honour with my craft the Mother of God in her monastery. Since others honour her with chant, then I will serve with tumbling."

He takes off his cowl, and removes his garments,

placing them near the altar, but so that his body be not naked he dons a tunic, very thin and fine, of scarce more substance than a shirt. So, light and comely of body, with gown girt closely about his loins, he comes before the Image right humbly. Then raising his eyes, "Lady," said he, "to your fair charge I give my body and my soul. Sweet Queen, sweet Lady, scorn not the thing I know, for with the help of God I will essay to serve you in good faith, even as I may. I cannot read your Hours nor chant your praise, but at the least I can set before you what art I have. Now will I be as the lamb that plays and skips before his mother. Oh, Lady, who art nowise bitter to those who serve you with a good intent, that which thy servant is, that he is for you."

Then commenced he his merry play, leaping low and small, tall and high, over and under. Then once more he knelt upon his knees before the statue, and meekly bowed his head. "Ha!" said he, "most gracious Queen, of your pity and your charity scorn not this my service." Again he leaped and played, and for holiday and festival, made the somersault of Metz. Again he bowed before the Image, did reverence, and paid it all the honour that he might. Afterwards he did the French vault, then the vault of Champagne, then the Spanish vault, then the vaults they love in Brittany, then the vault of Lorraine, and all these feats he did as best he was able. Afterwards he did the Roman vault, and then, with hands before his brow, danced daintily before the altar, gazing with a humble heart at the statue of God's Mother. "Lady," said he, "I set before you a fair play. This travail I do for you alone; so help me God, for you, Lady, and your Son.

Think not I tumble for my own delight; but I serve you, and look for no other guerdon on my carpet. My brothers serve you, yea, and so do I. Lady, scorn not your villein, for he toils for your good pleasure; and, Lady, you are my delight and the sweetness of the world." Then he walked on his two hands, with his feet in the air, and his head near the ground. He twirled with his feet, and wept with his eyes. "Lady," said he, "I worship you with heart, with body, feet and hands, for this I can neither add to nor take away. Now am I your very minstrel. Others may chant your praises in the church but here in the crypt will I tumble for your delight. Lady, lead me truly in your way, and for the love of God hold me not in utter despite." Then he smote upon his breast, he sighed and wept most tenderly, since he knew no better prayer than tears. Then he turned him about, and leaped once again. "Lady," said he, "as God is my Saviour, never have I turned this somersault before. Never has tumbler done such a feat, and, certes, it is not bad. Lady, what delight is his who may harbour with you in your glorious manor. For God's love, Lady, grant me such fair hostelry, since I am yours, and am nothing of my own." Once again he did the vault of Metz; again he danced and tumbled. Then when the chants rose louder from the choir, he, too, forced the note, and put forward all his skill. So long as the priest was about that Mass, so long his flesh endured to dance, and leap and spring, till at the last, nigh fainting, he could stand no longer upon his feet, but fell for weariness on the ground. From head to heel sweat stood upon him, drop by drop, as blood falls from meat turning upon the hearth. "Lady," said he, "I can no more, but truly will I seek you again." Fire consumed him utterly. He took his habit once more, and when he was wrapped close therein, he rose to his feet, and bending low before the statue, went his way. "Farewell," said he, "gentlest Friend. For God's love take it not to heart, for so I may I will soon return. Not one Hour shall pass but that I will serve you with right good will, so I may come, and so my service is pleasing in your sight." Thus he went from the crypt, yet gazing on his Lady. "Lady," said he, "my heart is sore that I cannot read your Hours. How would I love them for love of you, most gentle Lady! Into your care I commend my soul and my body."

In this fashion passed many days, for at every Hour he sought the crypt to do service, and pay homage before the Image. His service was so much to his mind that never once was he too weary to set out his most cunning feats to distract the Mother of God, nor did he ever wish for other play than this. Now, doubtless, the monks knew well enough that day by day he sought the crypt, but not a man on earth—save God alone—was aware of aught that passed there; neither would he, for all the wealth of the world, have let his goings in be seen, save by the Lord his God alone. For truly he believed that were his secret once espied he would be hunted from the cloister, and flung once more into the foul, sinful world, and for his part he was more fain to fall on death than to suffer any taint of sin. But God considering his simplicity, his sorrow for all he had wrought amiss, and the love which moved him to this deed, would that this toil should be known; and the Lord willed that the work of His friend should be made plain to men, for the glory of the Mother whom he worshipped, and so that all men should know and hear, and receive that God refuses none who seeks His face in love, however low his degree, save only he love God and strive to do His will.

Now think you that the Lord would have accepted this service, had it not been done for love of Him? Verily and truly, no, however much this juggler tumbled; but God called him friend, because he loved Him much. Toil and labour, keep fast and vigil, sigh and weep, watch and pray, ply the sharp scourge, be diligent at Matins and at Mass, owe no man anything, give alms of all you have—and yet, if you love not God with all your heart, all these good deeds are so much loss—mark well my words—and profit you naught for the saving of your soul. Without charity and love, works avail a man nothing. God asks not gold, neither for silver, but only for love unfeigned in His people's hearts, and since the tumbler loved Him beyond measure, for this reason God was willing to accept his service.

Thus things went well with this good man for a great space. For more years than I know the count of, he lived greatly at his ease, but the time came when the good man was sorely vexed, for a certain monk thought upon him, and blamed him in his heart that he was never set in choir for Matins. The monk marvelled much at his absence, and said within himself that he would never rest till it was clear what manner of man this was, and how he spent the Hours, and for what service the convent gave him bread. So he spied and pried and followed, till he marked him plainly, sweating at his craft in just such fashion as you have

heard. "By my faith," said he, "this is a merry jest, and
a fairer festival than we observe altogether. Whilst
others are at prayers, and about the business of the
House, this tumbler dances daintily, as though one
had given him a hundred silver marks. He prides himself on being so nimble of foot, and thus he repays us
what he owes. Truly it is this for that; we chant for
him, and he tumbles for us. We throw him largesse:
he doles us alms. We weep his sins, and he dries our
eyes. Would that the monastery could see him, as I
do, with their very eyes; willingly therefore would I
fast till Vespers. Not one could refrain from mirth at
the sight of this simple fool doing himself to death
with his tumbling, for on himself he has no pity. Since
his folly is free from malice, may God grant it to him
as penance. Certainly I will not impute it to him as
sin, for in all simplicity and good faith, I firmly believe, he does this thing, so that he may deserve his
bread." So the monk saw with his very eyes how the
tumbler did service at all the Hours, without pause
or rest, and he laughed with pure mirth and delight,
for in his heart was joy and pity.

The monk went straight to the Abbot and told him
the thing from beginning to end, just as you have
heard. The Abbot got him on his feet, and said to the
monk, "By holy obedience I bid you hold your peace,
and tell not this tale abroad against your brother. I
lay on you my strict command to speak of this matter
to none, save me. Come now, we will go forthwith
to see what this can be, and let us pray the Heavenly
King, and His very sweet, dear Mother, so precious
and so bright, that in her gentleness she will plead

with her Son, her Father, and her Lord, that I may look on this work—if thus it pleases Him—so that the good man be not wrongly blamed, and that God may be the more beloved, yet so that thus is His good pleasure." Then they secretly sought the crypt, and found a privy place near the altar, where they could see, and yet not be seen. From there the Abbot and his monk marked the business of the penitent. They saw the vaults he varied so cunningly, his nimble leaping and his dancing, his salutations of Our Lady, and his springing and his bounding, till he was nigh to faint. So weak was he that he sank on the ground, all outworn, and the sweat fell from his body upon the pavement of the crypt. But presently, in this his need, came she, his refuge, to his aid. Well she knew that guileless heart.

Whilst the Abbot looked, forthwith there came down from the vault a Dame so glorious, that certainly no man had seen one so precious, nor so richly crowned. She was more beautiful than the daughters of men, and her vesture was heavy with gold and gleaming stones. In her train came the hosts of Heaven, angel and archangel also; and these pressed close about the minstrel, and solaced and refreshed him. When their shining ranks drew near, peace fell upon his heart; for they contended to do him service, and were the servants of the servitor of that Dame who is the rarest Jewel of God. Then the sweet and courteous Queen herself took a white napkin in her hand, and with it gently fanned her minstrel before the altar. Courteous and debonair, the Lady refreshed his neck, his body and his brow. Meekly she served him as a handmaid in his need. But these things were hidden from the good man, for he neither saw nor knew that about him stood so fair a company.

The holy angels honour him greatly, but they can no longer stay, for their Lady turns to go. She blesses her minstrel with the sign of God, and the holy angels throng about her, still gazing back with delight upon their companion, for they await the hour when God shall release him from the burden of the world, and they possess his soul.

This marvel the Abbot and his monk saw at least four times, and thus at each Hour came the Mother of God with aid and succour for her man. Never doth she fail her servants in their need. Great joy had the Abbot that this thing was made plain to him. But the monk was filled with shame, since God had shown His pleasure in the service of His poor fool. His confusion burnt him like fire. "Dominus," said he to the Abbot, "grant me grace. Certainly this is a holy man, and since I have judged him amiss, it is very right that my body should smart. Give me now fast or vigil or the scourge, for without question he is a saint. We are witnesses to the whole matter, nor is it possible that we can be deceived." But the Abbot replied, "You speak truly, for God has made us to know that He has bound him with the cords of love. So I lay my commandment upon you, in virtue of obedience, and under pain of your person, that you tell no word to any man of that you have seen, save to God alone and me." "Lord," said he, "thus I will do." On these words they turned them, and hastened from the crypt; and the good man. having brought his tumbling to an end, presently clothed himself in his habit, and joyously went his way to the monastery.

Thus time went and returned, till it chanced that in a little while the Abbot sent for him who was so filled with virtue. When he heard that he was bidden of the Abbot, his heart was sore with grief, for he could think of nothing profitable to say. "Alas!" said he, "I am undone; not a day of my days but I shall know misery and sorrow and shame, for well I trow that my service is not pleasing to God. Alas! plainly doth He show that it displeases Him, since He causes the truth to be made clear. Could I believe that such work and play as mine could give delight to the mighty God! He had no pleasure therein, and all my toil was thrown away. Ah me, what shall I do? what shall I say? Fair, gentle God, what portion will be mine? Either shall I die in shame, or else shall I be banished from this place, and set up as a mark to the world and all the evil thereof. Sweet Lady, St. Mary, since I am all bewildered, and since there is none to give me counsel, Lady, come thou to my aid. Fair, gentle God, help me in my need. Stay not, neither tarry, but come quickly with Your Mother. For God's love, come not without her, but hasten both to me in my peril, for truly I know not what to plead. Before one word can pass my lips, surely will they bid me 'Begone.' Wretched that I am, what reply is he to make who has no advocate? Yet, why this dole, since go I must?" He came before the Abbot, with the tears yet wet upon his cheeks, and he was still weeping when he knelt upon the ground. "Lord," prayed he, "for the love of God deal not harshly with me. Would you send me from your door? Tell me what you would have me do, and thus it shall be done." Then replied the Abbot, "Answer me truly. Winter and summer have you lived here for a great space; now, tell me, what service have you given, and how have you deserved your bread?" "Alas!" said the tumbler, "well I knew that quickly I should be put upon the street when once this business was heard of you, and that you would keep me no more. Lord," said he, "I take my leave. Miserable I am, and miserable shall I ever be. Never yet have I made a penny for all my juggling." But the Abbot answered, "Not so said I; but I ask and require of you—nay, more, by virtue of holy obedience I command you—to seek within your conscience and tell me truly by what craft you have furthered the business of our monastery." "Lord," cried he, "now have you slain me, for this commandment is a sword." Then he laid bare before the Abbot the story of his days, from the first thing to the last, whatsoever pain it cost him; not a word did he leave out, but he told it all without a pause, just as I have told you the tale. He told it with clasped hands, and with tears, and at the close he kissed the Abbot's feet, and sighed.

The holy Abbot leaned above him, and, all in tears, raised him up, kissing both his eyes. "Brother," said he, "hold now your peace, for I make with you this true covenant, that you shall ever be of our monastery. God grant, rather, that we may be of yours, for all the worship you have brought to ours. I and you will call each other friend. Fair, sweet brother, pray you for me, and I for my part will pray for you. And now I pray

you, my swet friend, and lay this bidding upon you,
without pretence, that you continue to do your service, even as you were wont heretofore—yea, and with
greater craft yet, if so you may." "Lord," said he,
"truly is this so?" "Yea," said the Abbot, "and verily."
So he charged him, under peril of discipline, to put
all doubts from his mind; for which reason the good
man rejoiced so greatly that, as telleth the rhyme, he
was all bemused, so that the blood left his cheeks, and
his knees failed beneath him. When his courage came
back, his very heart thrilled with joy; but so perilous
was that quickening that therefrom he shortly died.
But theretofore with a good heart he went about his
service without rest, and Matins and Vespers, night
and day, he missed no Hour till he became too sick to
perform his office. So sore was his sickness upon him
that he might not rise from his bed. Marvellous was
the shame he proved when no more was he able to
pay his rent. This was the grief that lay the heaviest
upon him, for of his sickness he spake never a word,
but he feared greatly lest he should fall from grace
since he travailed no longer at his craft. He reckoned
himself an idle man, and prayed God to take him to
Himself before the sluggard might come to blame. For
it was bitter to him to consider that all about him
knew his case, so bitter that the burden was heavier
than his heart could bear, yet there without remedy he
must lie. The holy Abbot does him all honour; he
and his monks chant the Hours about his bed, and in
these praises of God he felt such delight that not for
them would he have taken the province of Poitou, so
great was his happiness therein. Fair and contrite was

his confession, but still he was not at peace; yet why say more of this, for the hour had struck, and he must rise and go.

The Abbot was in that cell with all his monks; there, too, was company of many a priest and many a canon. These all humbly watched the dying man, and saw with open eyes this wonder happen. Clear to their very sight, about that lowly bed, stood the Mother of God, with angel and archangel, to wait the passing of his soul. Over against them were set, like wild beasts, devils and the Adversary, so they might snatch his spirit. I speak not to you in parable. But little profit had they for all their coming, their waiting, and their straining on the leash. Never might they have part in such a soul as his. When the soul took leave of his body, it fell not in their hands at all, for the Mother of God gathered it to her bosom, and the holy angels thronging round, quired for joy, as the bright train swept to Heaven with its burthen, according to the will of God. To these things the whole of the monastery was witness, besides such others as were there. So knew they and perceived that God sought no more to hide the love He bore to His poor servant, but rather would that his virtues should be plain to each man in that place; and very wonderful and joyful seemed this deed to them. Then with meet reverence they bore the body on its bier within the abbey church, and with high pomp commended their brother to the care of God; nor was there monk who did not chant or read his portion that day within the choir of the mighty church.

Thus with great honour they laid him to his rest, and kept his holy body amongst them as a relic. At

that time spake the Abbot plainly to their ears, telling
them the story of this tumbler and of all his life, just
as you have heard, and of all that he himself beheld
within the crypt. No brother but kept awake during
that sermon. "Certes," said they, "easy is it to give
credence to such a tale; nor should any doubt your
words, seeing that the truth bears testimony to itself,
and witness comes with need; yea, without any doubt
have we full assurance that his discipline is done."
Great joy amongst themselves have all within that
place.

Thus endeth the story of the minstrel. Fair was his
tumbling, fair was his service, for thereby gained he
such high honour as is above all earthly gain. So the
holy Fathers narrate that in such fashion these things
chanced to this minstrel. Now, therefore, let us pray
to God—He Who is above all other—that He may
grant us so to do such faithful service that we may win
the guerdon of His love.

Here endeth the Tumbler of Our Lady.

THE LAY OF THE LITTLE BIRD

ONCE upon a time, more than a hundred years ago, there lived a rich villein whose name I cannot now tell, who owned meadows and woods and waters, and all things which go to the making of a rich man. His manor was so fair and so delightsome that all the world did not contain its peer. My true story would seem to you but idle fable if I set its beauty before you, for verily I believe that never yet was built so strong a keep and so gracious a tower. A river flowed around this fair domain, and enclosed an orchard planted with all manner of fruitful trees. This sweet fief was builded by a certain knight, whose heir sold it to a villein; for thus pass baronies from hand to hand, and town and manor change their master, always falling from bad to worse. The orchard was fair beyond content. Herbs grew there of every fashion, more than I am able to name. But at least I can tell you that so sweet was the savour of roses and other flowers and simples, that sick persons, borne within that garden in a litter, walked forth sound and well for having passed the night in so lovely a place. Indeed, so smooth and level was the sward, so tall the trees, so various the fruit, that the cunning gardener must surely have been a magician, as appears by certain infallible proofs.

Now in the middle of this great orchard sprang a fountain of clear, pure water. It boiled forth out of the ground, but was always colder than any marble. Tall trees stood about the well, and their leafy branch-

es made a cool shadow there, even during the longest
day of summer heat. Not a ray of the sun fell within
that spot, though it were the month of May, so
thick and close was the leafage. Of all these trees the
fairest and the most pleasant was a pine. To this pine
came a singing bird twice every day for ease of heart.
Early in the morning he came, when monks chant
their matins, and again in the evening, a little after
vespers. He was smaller than a sparrow, but larger than a wren, and he sang so sweetly that neither
lark nor nightingale nor black bird, nay, nor siren
even, was so grateful to the ear. He sang lays and bal-
lads, and the newest refrain of the minstrel and the
spinner at her wheel. Sweeter was his tune than harp
or viol, and gayer than the country dance. No man
had heard so marvellous a thing; for such was the
virtue in his song that the saddest and the most dolent
forgot to grieve whilst he listened to the tune, love
flowered sweetly in his heart, and for a space he was
rich and happy as any emperor or king, though but a
burgess of the city or a villein of the field. Yea, if that
ditty had lasted a hundred years, yet would he have
stayed the century through to listen to so lovely a song,
for it gave to every man whilst he hearkened, love,
and riches, and his heart's desire.

But all the beauty of the pleasaunce drew its being
from the song of the bird; for from his chant flowed
love which gives its shadow to the tree, its healing to
the simple, and its colour to the flower. Without that
song the fountain would have ceased to spring, and
the green garden become a little dry dust, for in its
sweetness lay all their virtue.

The villein, who was lord of this domain, walked

every day within his garden to hearken to the bird. On a certain morning he came to the well to bathe his face in the cold spring, and the bird, hidden close within the pine branches, poured out his full heart in a delightful lay, from which rich profit might be drawn.

"Listen," chanted the bird in his own tongue, "listen to my voice, oh, knight, and clerk, and layman, ye who concern yourselves with love, and suffer with its dolours: listen, also, ye maidens, fair and coy and gracious, who seek first the gifts and beauty of the world. I speak truth and do not lie. Closer should you cleave to God than to any earthly lover, right willingly should you seek His altar, more firmly should you hold to His commandment than to any mortal's pleasure. So you serve God and Love in such fashion, no harm can come to any, for God and Love are one. God loves sense and chivalry; and Love holds them not in despite. God hates pride and false seeming; and Love loveth loyalty. God praiseth honour and courtesy; and fair Love disdaineth them not. God lendeth His ear to prayer; neither doth Love refuse it her heart. God granteth largesse to the generous; but the grudging man, and the envious, the felon and the wrathful, doth He abhor. But courtesy and honour, good sense and loyalty, are the leal vassals of Love, and so you hold truly to them, God and the beauty of the world shall be added to you besides."

Thus told the bird in his song.

But when he saw the villein beneath the pine hearkening to his words, straight he changed his note, for well he knew him to be covetous and disloyal, and so he sang in quite another fashion.

"Oh, river, cease to flow; crumble, thou manor, keep and tower; let the grass wither with the rose, and the tall tree stand bare, for the gentle dames and knights come no more who once delighted in my song, and to whom this fountain was dear. In place of the brave and generous knights, set upon honour, stands this envious churl, greedy of naught but money. Those came to hear my song for solace, and for love of love; he but to eat and drink the more, and for ease of his gluttony."

And when the bird had thus spoken he took his flight.

Now the villein, who had listened to this song, thought within himself that might he snare so marvellous a bird, very easily could he sell him at a great price; or if he might not sell him, at least he could set him fast in a cage and hearken his lay at pleasure both early and late. So he climbed within the tree and sought and searched and pried until he marked the branch from whence the bird was wont to sing. There he set a cunning snare, and waited to see what time should make clear. At the hour of vespers the bird returned to the orchard, and lighting upon the branch was fast taken in the net. Then the villein came forth, and mounting quickly, joyously seized him in his hand.

"Small profit will you have of your labour," said the bird, "for I can pay but a poor ransom."

"At least I shall be paid in songs," answered the villein. "You were wont to sing for your own pleasure, now you will carol for mine."

"Think not so," replied the bird. "He who is used to the freedom of wood and meadow and river cannot live prisoned in a cage. What solace may I find there, or joy? Open your hand, fair sweet friend, for be assured no captive has a heart for songs."

"By my faith, then, you shall be served at table."

"Never will you have dined worse, for there is nothing of me. I pray you to let me go, for it were a sin to slay me."

"By my faith, you talk and talk; the more you plead, the less will I grant."

"Certes," answered the bird, "you are in your right, for such is the law. Many a time have I heard tell that the uncharitable granteth no alms. But there is a proverb that teaches that often man gives in his own interest what cannot be taken from him by force. Now, if you release me from this net I will make you free of three secrets which are little known to men of your lineage, and from which you may draw much profit."

"Tell me these secrets," said the villein, "and I will open my hand."

"Such faith have I in you," answered the bird, "that I will speak only when you free me from the snare."

The villein opened his hand, and the bird flew to a place of surety. His feathers were all ruffled, for he had been grossly handled by a glove not of silk but of wool, so he preened and plumed himself carefully with his beak. But the villein grew impatient, and urged him to pay his ransom. Now the bird was full of guile, so presently he made answer to the churl.

"Hear now the first of my three weighty secrets— Do not believe all that you may hear."

The villein frowned with anger, and answered that he knew it well.

"Fair friend, forget it never," replied the bird.

"Much I fear that I did foolishly in letting you from the snare. This secret was plain to me before; but now tell me the two others."

"They are fair and wise," said the bird. "Listen well to my second weighty secret—Do not regret what you have never lost."

"You mock me," cried the villein, "and do wrong to the faith you plighted with me. You pledged your word to tell me three secrets known but little to men of such lineage as mine, and you give me musty proverbs told over by all the world. Certes, what manner of man is he who weeps over what he has never had!"

"Shall I tell it once again," replied the bird, "for great fear have I lest it should travel from your mind."

"By my head," answered the villein, "I am a fairer scholar than you think. These two proverbs have naught to teach me; but hold truly to our covenant and bargain, and let the third secret contain a graver matter."

"Listen well to my third secret," said the bird, "for he who receives it shall never be poor."

"Ah, tell me this secret quickly," cried the churl, "for it draws near the hour of meat, and truly, beyond all things, do I desire to grow rich."

Now when the bird heard him—

"This be thy punishment, oh, thou false churl—What you hold in your hand, never throw between your feet."

Then was the villein all wrathful; but when words came to him to speak, he said—

"And are these your three mighty secrets! Why, these are but children's riddles, which I have known

ever since I was born. You have but lied to me, and
of all your teaching had I full knowledge long before."

"By my faith," responded the bird, "had you known
my third secret never would you have let me from
your hand."

"You say well," said the villein, "but at least knew
I the two other proverbs."

"Ah," said the bird, with malice, "but this proverb
was worth a hundred of the others."

"In what manner?" inquired the villein.

"What, know you not what has chanced to you? Had
you slain me when I was in your power that day
would have been the happiest of your life. For in my
body is a jewel, so precious and so rare, that it weighs
at least three ounces. Yea, the virtue of this stone is
such that he who owns it has but to wish, and lo, his
desire is fulfilled."

When the villein heard this thing he beat upon his
breast, he tore his raiment, and disfigured his face
with his nails, crying out that he was wretched and
undone. The bird from his refuge in the tree rejoiced greatly to observe the churl's miserable plight,
and said nothing till his enemy's clothes were torn to
rags, and his hands sore wounded in many places.
Then he spake—

"Miserable churl, when you held me fast in your
rude hand, easy was it to know that I was no larger
than a sparrow or a finch, and weighed less than half
an ounce. How, then, could a precious stone, three
ounces in weight, be hid in my body? Now will I
prove to you that of my three secrets you understood
not a single one. You asked me what man was fool
enough to weep over that which he had never lost,

and even now I watch your tears fall for a jewel which was never yours, nor will be ever. You had faith in all that I was pleased to tell you, trusting all you heard; and in your folly you flung the bird you held in hand between your very feet. Fair friend, con over my three secrets, and learn wisdom even from the counsel of a bird."

When he had spoken thus he took his flight, and from that hour the orchard knew him no more. With the ceasing of his song the leaves withered from the pine, the garden became a little dry dust, and the fountain forgot to flow. Thus the rich villein lost his pleasaunce, which once was fair beyond content. And remember well, fair lords and dames, that truly speaks the proverb, "He who covet another's good, oft loses his own," as we may learn from the "Lay of the Little Bird."

THE DIVIDED HORSECLOTH

EACH owes it to his fellows to tell as best he may, or, better still, to write with fair enticing words, such deeds and adventures as are good and profitable for us to know. For as men come and go about their business in the world, many things are told them which it is seemly to keep in remembrance. Therefore, it becomes those who say and relate, diligently and with fair intent to keep such matters in thought and study, even as did our fathers before us. Theirs is the school to which we all should pass, and he who would prove an apt scholar, and live beyond his day, must not be idle at his task. But the world dims our fine gold: the minstrel is slothful, and singers forget to sing, because of the pain and travail which go to the finding of their songs. So without waiting for any to-morrow, I will bring before you a certain adventure which chanced, even as it was told to me.

Some seven years ago it befell that a rich burgess of Abbeville departed from the town, together with his wife, his only son, and all his wealth, his goods and plenishing. This he did like a prudent man, since he found himself at enmity with men who were stronger and of more substance than he. So, fearing lest a worse thing should bechance him, from Abbeville he went up to Paris. There he sought a shop and dwelling, and paying his service, made himself vassal and burgess of the King. The merchant was diligent and courteous, his wife smiling and gracious, and their son was not given over to folly, but went soberly, even as his parents taught him. Much were they praised of their neighbours, and those who lived in the same street often set foot in their dwelling. For very greatly are those loved and esteemed by their fellows who are courteous in speech and address. He who has fair words in his mouth receives again sweet words in his ear, and foul words and foul deeds bring naught but bitterness and railing. Thus was it with this prudent merchant. For more than seven years he went about his business, buying and selling, concerning himself with matters of which he had full knowledge, putting by of his earnings a little every day, like a wise and worthy citizen. So this wealthy merchant lived a happy blameless life, till, by the will of God, his wife was taken from him, who had been his companion for some thirty years. Now these parents had but one only child, a son, even as I have told you before. Very grievously did he mourn the death of her who had cherished him so softly, and lamented his mother with many tears, till he came nigh to swoon. Then, to put a little comfort in his heart, his father said to him—

"Fair son, thy mother is dead, and we will pray to God that He grant her mercy in that day. But dry now thine eyes and thy face, for tears can profit thee nothing. By that road we all must go, neither can any man pass Death upon the way, nor return to bring us any word. Fair son, for thee there is goodly comfort. Thou art a young bachelor, and it is time to take thee a wife. I am full of years, and so I may find thee a fair marriage in an honourable house I will endow thee with my substance. I will now seek a bride for thee of birth and breeding—one of family and descent, one come of ancient race, with relations and friends a gracious company, a wife from honest folk and from an honest home. There, where it is good and profitable to be, I will set thee gladly, nor of wealth and moneys shalt thou find a lack."

Now in that place were three brethren, knights of high lineage, cousins to mighty lords of peerage, bearing rich and honourable blazons on their shields. But these knights had no heritage, since they had pawned all that they owned of woods and houses and lands, the better to take their pleasure at the tourney. Passing heavy and tormented were these brethren because in no wise might they redeem their pledge. The eldest of these brothers had a daughter, but the mother of the maid was dead. Now this damsel owned in Paris a certain fair house, over against the mansion of the wealthy merchant. The house was not of her father's heritage, but came to her from her mother, who had put the maid in ward to guardians, so that the house was free from pledge. She received in rent therefrom the sum of twenty Paris pounds every year, and her dues were paid her right willingly. So the merchant, esteeming her a lady of family and estate, demanded her hand in marriage of her father and of all her friends. The knight inquired in his turn of the means and substance of the merchant, who answered very frankly—

"In merchandise and in moneys I have near upon fifteen hundred pounds. Should I tell you that I had more, I should lie, and speak not the truth. I have besides one hundred Paris pounds, which I have gained in honest dealings. Of all this I will give my son the half."

"Fair sir," made answer the knight, "in no wise can this be agreed to. Had you become a Templar, or a White or a Black monk you would have granted the whole of your wealth either to the Temple or your Abbey. By my faith, we cannot consent to so grudging an offer, certes, sir merchant, no."

"Tell me then what you would have me do."

"Very willingly, fair, dear sir. We would that you grant to your son the sum and total of your substance, so that he be seized of all your wealth, and this in such fashion that neither you, nor any in your name, may claim return of any part thereof. If you consent to this the marriage can be made, but otherwise he shall never wed our child and niece."

The merchant turned this over for a while, now looking upon his son, now deep in thought. But very badly he was served of all his thought and pondering. For at the last he made reply to him and said—

"Lord, it shall even be done according to your will. This is our covenant and bargain, that so your daughter is given to my son I will grant him all that I have of worth. I take this company as witness that here I strip myself of everything I own, so that naught is mine, but all is his, of what I once was seized and possessed."

Thus before the witnesses he divested himself utterly of all his wealth, and became naked as a peeled wand in the eyes of the world, for this merchant now had neither purse nor penny, nor wherewithal to break his fast, save it were given him by his son. So when the words were spoken and the merchant altogether spoiled, then the knight took his daughter by the hand and handfasted her with the bachelor, and she became his wife.

For two years after this marriage the husband and the dame lived a quiet and peaceful life. Then a fair son was born to the bachelor, and the lady cherished and guarded him fondly. With them dwelt the merchant in the same lodging, but very soon he perceived that he had given himself a mortal blow in despoiling himself of his substance to live on the charity of others. But perforce he remained of their household for more than twelve years, until the lad had grown up tall, and began to take notice, and to remember that which often he heard of the making of his father's marriage And well he promised himself that it should never go from mind.

The merchant was full of years. He leaned upon his staff, and went bent with age, as one who searches for his lost youth. His son was weary of his presence, and would gladly have paid for the spinning of his shroud. The dame, who was proud and disdainful, held him in utter despite, for greatly he was against her heart. Never was she silent, but always was she saying to her lord—

"Husband, for love of me, send your father upon his business. I lose all appetite just for the sight of him about the house."

"Wife," answered he, "this shall be done according to your wish."

So because of his wife's anger and importunity, he sought out his father straightway, and said—

"Father, father, get you gone from here. I tell you

that you must do the best you can, for we may no longer concern ourselves with you and your lodging. For twelve years and more we have given you food and raiment in our house. Now all is done, so rise and depart forthwith, and fend for yourself, as fend you must."

When the father heard these words he wept bitterly, and often he cursed the day and the hour in which he found he had lived too long.

"Ah, fair, sweet son, what is this thou sayest to me! For the love of God turn me not from thy door. I lie so close that thou canst not want my room. I require of thee neither seat in the chimney corner, nor soft bed of feathers, no, nor carpet on the floor; but only the attic, where I may bide on a little straw. Throw me not from thy house because I eat of thy bread, but feed me without grudging for the short while I have to live. In the eyes of God this charity will cover all thy sins better than if thou went in haircloth next the flesh."

"Fair father," replied the bachelor, "preach me no preachings, but get you forth at once, for reason that my wife would have you gone."

"Fair son, where then shall I go, who am esteemed of nothing worth?"

"Get you gone to the town, for amongst ten thousand others very easily you may light on good fortune. Very unlucky you will be if there you cannot find a way to live. Seek your fortune bravely. Perchance some of your friends and acquaintance will receive you into their houses."

"Son, how then shall men take me to their lodging, when you turn me from the house which I have given you? Why should the stranger welcome that guest whom the son chases from his door? Why should I be received gladly by him to whom I have given naught, when I am evilly entreated of the rich man for whose sake I go naked?"

"Father," said he, "right or wrong, I take the blame upon my own head; but go you must because it is according to my will."

Then the father grieved so bitterly that for a little his very heart would have broken. Weak as he was, he raised himself to his feet and went forth from the house, weeping.

"Son," said he, "I commend thee to God; but since thou wilt that I go, for the love of Him give me at least a portion of packing cloth to shelter me against the wind. I am asking no great matter; nothing but a little cloth to wrap about me, because I am but lightly clad, and fear to die for reason of the cold."

Then he who shrank from any grace of charity made reply—

"Father, I have no cloth, so neither can I bestow, nor have it taken from me."

"Fair, sweet son, my heart trembles within me, so greatly do I dread the cold. Give me, then, the cloth you spread upon your horse, so that I come to no evil."

So he, seeing that he might not rid himself of his father save by the granting of a gift, and being desirous above all that he should part, bade his son to fetch this horsecloth. When the lad heard his father's call he sprang to him, saying—

"Father, what is your pleasure?"

"Fair son," said he, "get you to the stable, and if you find it open give my father the covering that is upon

my horse. Give him the best cloth in the stable, so that
he may make himself a mantle or a habit, or any other
sort of cloak that pleases him."

Then the lad, who was thoughtful beyond his years,
made answer—

"Grandsire, come now with me."

So the merchant went with him to the stable, exceedingly heavy and wrathful. The lad chose the best
horsecloth he might find in the stable, the newest, the
largest, and the most fair; this he folded in two, and
drawing forth his knife, divided the cloth in two portions. Then he bestowed on his grandfather one half
of the sundered horsecloth.

"Fair child," said the old man, "what have you
done? Why have you cut the cloth that your father has
given me? Very cruelly have you treated me, for you
were bidden to give me the horsecloth whole. I shall
return and complain to my son thereof."

"Go where you will," replied the boy, "for certainly
you shall have nothing more from me."

The merchant went forth from the stable.

"Son," said he, "chastise now thy child, since he
counts thy word as nothing but an idle tale, and fears
not to disobey thy commandment. Dost thou not see
that he keeps one half of the horsecloth?"

"Plague take thee!" cried the father; "give him all
the cloth."

"Certes," replied the boy, "that will I never do, for
how then shall you be paid? Rather will I keep the
half until I am grown a man, and then give it to you.
For just as you have chased him from your house, so
I will put you from my door. Even as he has bestowed
on you all his wealth, so, in my turn, will I require of

you all your substance. Naught from me shall you carry away, save that only which you have granted to him. If you leave him to die in his misery, I wait my day, and surely will leave you to perish in yours."

The father listened to these words, and at the end sighed heavily. He repented him of the evil that he purposed, and from the parable that his child had spoken took heed and warning. Turning himself about towards the merchant, he said—

"Father, return to my house. Sin and the Enemy thought to have caught me in the snare, but, please God, I have escaped from the fowler. You are master and lord, and I render all that I have received into your hands. If my wife cannot live with you in quiet, then you shall be served and cherished elsewhere. Chimney corner, and carpet, pillow and bed of feathers, at your ease you shall have pleasure in them all. I take St. Martin to witness that never will I drink stoup of wine, never carve morsel from dish, but that yours shall be the richer portion. Henceforth you shall live softly in the ceiled chamber, near by a blazing fire, clad warmly in your furred robe, even as I. And all this is not of charity, but of your right, for, fair sweet father, if I am rich it is because of your substance."

Thus the brave witness and the open remonstrance of a child freed his father from the bad thoughts that he harboured. And deeply should this adventure be considered of those who are about to marry their children. Let them not strip themselves so bare as to have nothing left. For he who gives all, and depends upon the charity of others, prepares a rod for his own back.

SIR HUGH OF TABARIE

IN the years when Saladin was King, there lived a Prince in Galilee, who was named Sir Hugh of Tabarie. On a day he was with other Christian men who gave battle to the Turks, and, since it pleased God to cast His chivalry behind Him, Sir Hugh was taken prisoner, and many another stout knight with him. When dusk closed down on the field, the Prince was led before Saladin, who, calling him straightway to mind, rejoiced greatly and cried—

"Ah, Sir Hugh, now are you taken."

"Sire," answered the brave knight, "the greater grief is mine."

"By my faith, Hugh, every reason have you for grief, since you must either pay your ransom or die."

"Sire, I am more fain to pay ransom than to die, if by any means I may find the price you require of me."

"Is that truly so?" said the King.

"Sire," said Sir Hugh, "in the fewest words, what is the sum you demand of me?"

"I ask of you," replied the King, "one hundred thousand besants."

"Sire, such a sum is too great a ransom for a man of my lands to pay."

"Hugh," said the King, "you are so good a knight, and so hardy, that there is none who hears of your prison and this ransom, but will gladly send of his riches for your ease."

"Sire," said he, "since thus it must be, I promise to

pay the sum you require, but what time do you grant me to find so mighty a ransom?"

"Hugh," said the King, "I accord you the grace of one year. If within the year you count me out the tale of these besants, I will take it gladly; but if you fail to gain it, then must you return to your prison, and I will hold you more willingly still."

"Sire, I pledge my word and my faith. Now deliver me such a safe conduct that I may return in surety to my own land."

"Hugh, before you part I have a privy word to speak to you."

"Sire, with all my heart, and where?"

"In this tent, close by."

When they were entered into the pavilion, the Emperor Saladin sought to know of Sir Hugh in what fashion a man was made knight of the Christian chivalry, and required of him that he should show it to his eyes.

"Sire, whom then should I dub knight?"

"Myself," answered the King.

"Sire, God forbid that I should be so false as to confer so high a gift and so fair a lordship even upon the body of so mighty a prince as you."

"But wherefore?" said the King.

"For reason, sire, that your body is but an empty vessel."

"Empty of what, Sir Hugh?"

"Sire, of Christianity and of baptism."

"Hugh," said he, "think not hardly of me because of this. You are in my hand, and if you do the thing that I require of you, what man is there to blame you greatly when you return to your own realm. I seek this

grace of you, rather than of another, because you are
the stoutest and most perfect knight that ever I may
meet."

"Sire," said he, "I will show you what you seek to
know, for were it but the will of God that you were a
christened man, our chivalry would bear in you its
fairest flower."

"Hugh," said he, "that may not be."

Thereupon Sir Hugh made ready all things necessary for the making of a knight; and having trimmed
the hair and beard of the King in seemly fashion, he
caused him to enter within a bath, and inquired—

"Sire, do you understand the meaning of this
water?"

"Hugh, of this I know nothing."

"Sire, as the little child comes forth from the waters
of baptism clean of sin, so should you issue from this
bath washed pure of all stain and villainy."

"By the law of the Prophet, Sir Hugh, it is a fair
beginning."

Then Sir Hugh brought the Sultan before an untouched bed, and having laid him therein, he said—

"Sire, this bed is the promise of that long rest in
Paradise which you must gain by the toils of chivalry."

So when the King had lain softly therein for a little
space, Sir Hugh caused him to stand upon his feet,
and having clothed him in a fair white vesture of lin-
en and of silk, said—

"Sire, this spotless stole you first put on is but the
symbol of a body held and guarded clean."

Afterwards he set upon the King a gown of scarlet
silk, and said—

"Sire, this vermeïl robe keeps ever in your mind

the blood a knight must shed in the service of his God and the defence of Holy Church."

Then taking the King's feet in his hands, he drew thereon shoes of brown leather, saying—

"Sire, these brown shoes with which you are shod, signify the colour of that earth from which you came, and to which you must return; for whatever degree God permits you to attain, remember, O mortal man, that you are but dust."

Then Sir Hugh raised the Sultan to his feet, and girt him with a white baldrick, saying—

"Sire, this white cincture I belt about your loins is the type of that chastity with which you must be girded withal. For he who would be worthy of such dignity as this must ever keep his body pure as any maid."

After this was brought to Sir Hugh a pair of golden spurs, and these he did upon the shoes with which the Sultan was shod, saying—

"Sire, so swiftly as the destrier plunges in the fray at the prick of these spurs, so swiftly, so joyously, should you fight as a soldier of God for the defence of Holy Church."

Then at the last Hugh took a sword, and holding it before the King, said—

"Sire, know you the three lessons of this glaive?"

"What lessons are these?"

"Courage, justice and loyalty. The cross at the hilt of his sword gives courage to the bearer, for when the brave knight girds his sword upon him he neither can, nor should, fear the strong Adversary himself. Again, sire, the two sharp edges of the blade teach loyalty and justice, for the office of chivalry is this, to sustain the weak against the strong, the poor before the rich, uprightly and loyally."

The King listened to all these words very heedfully, and at the end inquired if there was nothing more that went to the making of a knight.

"Sire, there is one thing else, but that I dare not do."

"What thing is this?"

"It is the accolade."

"Grant me now this accolade, and tell me the meaning thereof."

"Sire, the accolade is a blow upon the neck given with a sword, and the significance thereof is that the newly made knight may always bear in mind the lord who did him that great courtesy. But such a stroke will I not deal to you, for it is not seemly, since I am here your prisoner."

That night Saladin, the mighty Sultan, feasted in his chamber, with the fifty greatest lords of his realm, emirs, governors and admirals, and Sir Hugh of Tabarie sat on a cushion at his feet. At the close of the banquet Sir Hugh rose up before the King and said—

"Sire, grant me grace. I may not forget that you bade me to seek out all fair and honourable lords, since there is none who would not gladly come to my help in this matter of my ransom. But, fair Sir King, in all the world shall I never find a lord so wise, so hardy, and so courteous as yourself. Since you have taught me this lesson, it is but just and right that I should pray you to be the first to grant me aid herein."

Then Saladin laughed loudly out of a merry heart, and said—

"Pray God that the end be as sweet as the beginning. Truly, Sir Hugh, I will not have it on my conscience that you miss your ransom because of any meanness of mine, and therefore, without guile, for my part I will give you fifty thousand good besants."

Then the great Sultan rose from his throne, and taking Prince Hugh with him, came to each of the lords in turn—emir, governor and admiral—and prayed of him aid in the business of this ransom. So all the lords gave largely out of a good heart, in such measure that Sir Hugh presently acquitted himself of his ransom, and returned to his own realm from amongst the Paynim.

THE STORY OF KING FLORUS AND
OF THE FAIR JEHANE

HERE begins the story of a certain King who was named King Florus of Ausay. This King Florus was a very stout knight, and a gentleman of proud descent. He was wedded to the daughter of the Prince of Brabant, a gentlewoman of high lineage. Very fair was the maid when she became his dame, slender of shape and dainty of fashion, and the story telleth that she was but fifteen summers old when King Florus became her lord, and he was but of seventeen years. A right happy life they passed together, as becometh bride and groom who wed fondly in their youth; yet because he might have no child of her King Florus was often dolent, and she for her part was vexed full grievously. This lady was very gracious of person, and very devout towards God and Holy Church. She gave alms willingly, and was so charitable that she nourished and clothed the needy, kissing their hands and feet. Moreover, so constant and private in service was she to the lepers of the lazar house, both men and women, that the Holy Ghost dwelt within her. Her lord, King Florus, so long as his realm had peace, rode forth as knight-errant to all the tournaments in Allemaigne and France and many other lands of which the noise reached him; thereon he spent much treasure, and gained great honour thereby.

But now my tale ceases to speak of him, and telleth of a knight who dwelt in the marches of Flanders and of Hainault. This knight was wise in counsel, and brave of heart, very sure and trusty. He had to wife a right fair lady, of whom he had one daughter, young and fresh, named Jehane, a maid of some twelve years. Many sweet words were spoken of this maiden, for in all the country round was none so fair. Her mother prayed often to her lord that he should grant the girl in marriage, but so given were all his thoughts to the running of tourneys that he considered nothing of the trothing of his child, though his wife admonished him ever on his return from the jousts.

This knight had for squire a man named Robert, the bravest squire in any Christian realm. His prowess and his praise were such that oft he aided his lord to bear away the prize from the tournaments whereat he ran. So great was his praise that his lady spake him thus—

"Robert, more careth my lord for these joustings than for any words I speak, which thing is grievous to me, for I would that he gave care and pains to wed this daughter of mine. I pray you, therefore, for love of me, that if you may, you tell him that very ill he does, and is greatly to be blamed, not to marry his own fair child, for there is no knight of these parts, however rich his state, who would not gladly welcome such a bride."

"Lady," said Robert, "you have well spoken. Very readily will I speak thereof, and since my lord asks often of my counsel, every hope have I that he will take heed to my words."

"Robert," said the lady, "you will find me no niggard, so you do this task."

"Lady," said Robert, "your prayer is guerdon enough for me. Be assured I will do all that I may."

"I am content," returned the lady.

Now within a little space the knight made ready to fare to a tournament very far from his land. When he came to the field, he (with a certain knight in whose company he rode) was joined to one party, and his banner was carried to the lodging of his lord. The tilting began, and such deeds did the knight, by the cunning service of his squire, that he bore off the honour and the prize of that tourney from the one side and the other. On the second day the knight prepared to return to his own country; so Robert took him often to task and blamed him greatly that he had not bestowed his fair daughter in marriage. Having heard this many times, at the end his lord replied—

"Robert, thou and thy lady give me no peace in the matter of the marriage of my daughter; but at present I see and know of none in my parts to whom I am content to give her."

"Ah, sir," cried Robert, "there is no knight in your realm who would not receive her right joyously."

"Robert, fair friend, they are worth nothing, not one of them; neither will I bestow her there with my good will. I know of no man in the world who is worthy of her, save one man only, and he, forsooth, is no knight."

"Sir, tell me his name," answered Robert, "and I will find means to speak to him so privily that the marriage shall be made."

"Certes, Robert," returned the knight, "meseems thou art very desirous that my daughter shall be wedded."

"Sir," quoth Robert, "you speak truly, for it is full time."

"Robert," said the knight, "since thou art so hot to carol at her wedding, she shall soon enough be married if thou accord thereto."

"Certes, sir," said Robert, "right willingly will I consent thereto."

"To that you pledge your word?" demanded the knight.

"Truly, sir, yes," answered Robert.

"Robert, thou hast served me very faithfully, and ever have I found thee skilled and true. Such as I am, that thou hast made of me; for by thine aid at the tourneys have I gained five hundred pounds of rent. 'Twas but a short time since that I had but five hundred; whereas now I have one thousand pounds from rent of land. This, therefore, I owe to thee, and I acquit me of my debt by giving thee my fair daughter, so thou art willing to take her at my hand."

"Ah, sir," cried Robert, "for the pity of God, say not thus. I am too low a man to snatch at so high a maiden, nor dare I pretend to one so rich and gracious as my demoiselle, since there is no knight in all the realm, whate'er his breeding, who would not count it honour to be her lord."

"Robert, know of a surety that never shall knight of this country call her his; but I will bestow her on thee, if thou refusest her not, and for her dowry shall she bring thee four hundred pounds from rent of my lands."

"Ah, sir," said Robert, "you are pleased to make a mock of me."

"Robert," said the knight, "be assured this is no jest."

"Ah, sir, neither my lady nor her mighty kin will endure to consent thereto."

"Robert," said the knight, "this matter concerns none of them. Hold, I give thee my glove, and I invest thee with four hundred pounds of my land, and this is my warrant for the delivery thereof."

"Sir," said Robert, "I will not refuse so goodly a gift, since it is given with so true a heart."

"Robert," replied the knight, "the grant is sealed."

So the knight granted him his glove, and invested him with rights in that fair maiden and her land.

Thus they passed upon their ways until it fortuned that this knight returned to his own house. When he was entered therein, his wife—that comely dame—received him right sweetly, and said—

"Husband, for the love of God, give thought at this time to the marriage of our maid."

"Dame," said her lord, "thou hast spoken so often of this matter that I have trothed her already."

"Sir," inquired the lady, "to whom?"

"Certes, dame, I have pledged her to a man who will ever be loyal and true. I have given her to Robert, my squire."

"To Robert! Alas the day," quoth the lady. "Robert is but a naked man, nor is there a knight, however noble, in all this realm who would not have taken her gladly. Certainly Robert shall have none of her."

"Dame, have her he shall, for I have delivered to him as my daughter's portion four hundred pounds in rent of land, and all his rights therein I warrant and will maintain."

When the lady heard this thing she was sore troubled, and said to her lord that of a surety should Robert never possess her maid.

"Dame," said her husband, "have her he shall, with good will or with bad will, for I have made a covenant with him, and will carry out my bargain."

When the lady heard these words of her lord she sought her chamber, and wept and lamented very grievously. After her tears were shed then she sent to seek her brothers and other kinsmen of her house, and showed them of that thing her lord would do, and they said—

"Lady, what have we to do herein? We have no care to go counter to your lord, for he is a stout knight, weighty of counsel and heavy of hand. Moreover, can he not do as he will with his daughter, and his land besides? Know you well that for this cause will none of us hang shield about his neck."

"Alas," said the lady, "never may my heart find happiness again, if thus I lose my child. At the least, fair lords, I pray and require you to show him that should he make this marriage he acts not rightly, nor after his own honour."

"Lady," said they, "this we will do full willingly."

So they sought out the knight and acquitted themselves of their task, and he answered them in courteous wise—

"Fair lords, I will tell you what I can do for your love. So it be your pleasure, I will defer this marriage on such understanding as I now declare. You are great lords, and are rich in gold and lands. Moreover, you are near of kin to this fair maid of mine, whom very tenderly I love. If on your part you will endue her with four hundred pounds of rent on your lands, I, on mine, will disavow this bond of marriage, and will wed the girl according to your wise counsel."

"In the name of God," answered they with one accord, "would you spoil us of all the wealth in our wallets?"

"Since, then," replied the knight, "you may not do this thing, suffer me to do as I will with my own."

"Sir, with right good mind," answered they.

Then the knight sent for his chaplain, and before him affianced Robert and his fair daughter together, appointing a certain day for the marriage. But on the third day Robert prayed his lord that he would dub him knight, since it was not seemly that he should take a wife so fair and of such high station till he was of her degree. His lord agreed thereto with a glad heart, and on the morrow granted him his desire; therefore after the third day he married the fair maid with great joy and festival.

At the hour Messire Robert was made knight he spake thus to his lord—

"Sir, once when I was in grievous peril of death, I vowed to seek St. James's shrine on the morrow of that day I gained my spurs. I pray you be not wroth with me if to-morrow morn it becomes my honour to wend thither directly after this marriage, for in no wise will I fail to observe my vow."

"Certes, Messire Robert, if you do this despite to my daughter, and go lonely upon your road, very rightly will you be held to blame."

"Sir," said he, "so it pleases God, I shall soon return, but go I must on peril of my soul."

When a certain knight of the lord's household heard

these words, greatly he reproached Messire Robert for parting from his bride at such an hour, but Robert answered him that he durst not break his oath.

"Truly," said the knight, who was named Raoul, "truly if you wend thus to St. James's shrine, leaving so fair a bride but a wedded maid, very surely will I win her love ere you return. Certain proofs, moreover, will I give that I have had my way with her; and to this will I pledge my lands against the lands our lord has granted you, for mine are fully worth the rents of yours."

"My wife," answered Messire Robert, "does not come of a race to deal me so shrewd a wrong, and since I give no credence to your words, willingly will I make the wager, if so it pleases you."

"Yes," said Raoul, "and to this you pledge your faith?"

"Yea," said Messire Robert, "willingly. And you?"

"I, too, pledge my faith. Now let us seek our lord forthwith, and set before him our bargain."

"That is my desire also," said Messire Robert.

Then they went straight to their lord and laid before him this wager, and plighted troth to observe their covenant. So in the morning Messire Robert was married to the fair maiden, and when the bridal Mass was ended, incontinent he parted from the hall, without tasting the wedding meats, and set forth on his way, a pilgrim to Compostella.

Now ceaseth the tale to speak of him, and telleth of Raoul, who was hot in thought as to how he might gain the wager and have to do with the fair lady. So relateth the tale that the lady behaved very discreetly whilst her husband was on pilgrimage, for she spent much time upon her knees in church, praying God to bring her lord again. For his part Messire Raoul was in a heat in what manner he might win the wager, for more and more it seemed to him that he should lose his land. He sought speech with an old dame who attended on the lady, promising that so she brought him in such a place and hour that he might speak privily to Madame Jehane, and have his will, then he would deal so largely with her, that never in her life should she be poor.

"Certes, sir," said the crone, "you are so lovely a knight, so sweet in speech and so courteous, that verily it is my lady's duty to set her love upon you, and it will be my pleasure to toil in your service."

So the knight took forty sous from his pouch, and gave them to her that she might buy a kirtle. The old woman received them greedily, and hiding the money in a secret place promised to speak to her lady. The knight bade farewell, and went his way, but the crone tarried in that place, and when her lady entered from the church said straitly—

"Lady, for God's love, tell me truly, when my lord went to Compostella did he leave you a maid?"

"Why ask you such a question, Dame Hersent?"

"Because, lady, I believe you to be a virgin wife!"

"Certes, Dame Hersent, and that I am, nor do I know woman who would be aught else in my case."

"Lady," returned Dame Hersent, "ah, the pity of it! If you but knew the joy that women have in company of the man they love, you would say that there is no fonder happiness to be found on earth. Greatly I marvel, therefore, that you love not, *par amours*, seeing that every lady loveth with her friend. Were the thing but pleasing to you, fair falleth the chance, for well I know a knight, comely of person, sweet and wise of speech, who asks naught better than to set on you his love. Very rich is he, and lovelier far than the shamed recreant who has left you in this plight. If you are not too fearful to grant him grace, you can have of him all that you please to ask, and such joy moreover as no lady can hope for more."

Whilst the crone was speaking, the lady, who was but a woman, felt her senses stir within. Curiously she inquired who this knight should be.

"Who is he, lady? God above! one has no fear to cry his name! Who should it be but that lovely lord, so courteous, so bold, Messire Raoul, of your father's house, the sweetest heart of all the world."

"Dame Hersent," said the lady, "you will do well to let these words be, for I have no wish to do myself such wrong, neither come I of such stock as goes after shame."

"Dame," replied the old woman, "I know it well; but never can you have the joy of maid with man."

Thus ended their discourse; but presently Sir Raoul came again to the crone, and she made plain to him how she had spoken to her lady, and in what fashion she was answered.

"Dame Hersent," said the knight, "so should a virtuous lady reply; but I pray you speak again with her of this matter, for the archer does not wing the bird with a first arrow; and, stay, take these twenty sous, and buy a lining to your coat."

So that ancient dame took the gift, and wearied the lady with enticing words, but nothing came of all her proffers.

Slowly or quickly thus passed the days, till came the tidings that Sir Robert was on his way from Compostella, and was already near to Paris. Very speedily this news was noised abroad, and Sir Raoul, fearing greatly to lose his lands, again sought speech with the crone. Then said the old woman that in no wise could she snare the bird, but that for the great love she bore him this thing she would do—so he would recompense her service—namely, that she would put matters in such a case that none should be in the house save himself and the lady, and then he could act according to his pleasure, whether she would or whether she would not. So Raoul answered that he desired no other thing.

"This I will do," said the old woman. "Messire shall come again in eight days, and on that day shall my lady bathe within her bower. I will see that all her household are forth from the castle, so may you come privily to her chamber, and have your desire of her, whether she cry yea or whether she cry nay."

"You have fairly spoken," answered he.

Hard upon this came letters from Messire Robert that he would be at the castle on Sunday. On the Thursday, therefore, the crone caused the bath to be heated in the bower, and the lady disarrayed herself to enter therein. Then the old woman sent messages to Sir Raoul that he should come speedily, and moreover she caused all the household to go forth from that place. Sir Raoul came to the bower, and entering, saluted the lady, but she deigned no reply to his greeting, and said—

"Sir Raoul, of a truth I thank you for this courtesy, yet you might have asked if such a visit would be ac-

cording to my wish. Accursed may you be for a most
ungentle knight."

But Sir Raoul made reply—

"Madame, for God's sake have pity upon me, for
I die for love of you. Lady, as you hope for grace, so
grant grace to me."

"Sir Raoul," cried she, "never for pity will I grant
you this day, or any day, the grace of my love. Know
well that if you do not leave me alone in peace certainly will I tell your lord, my father, the honour that
you require of me, for I am no such woman as you
think."

"Nay, lady, is it so indeed?"

"Yes, and very surely," replied she.

Then Sir Raoul sprang forward, and clasping her
in his arms (for he was very mighty) bore her towards
her bed. As they strove he saw beneath her right
breast a black spot upon the groin, and thought within himself that here was certain proof that he had had
to do with her. But as he carried her towards the bed
his spurs caught within the serge valence about the
foot thereof, so that they fell together, the lord below
and the lady above; whereupon she rose lightly to her
feet, and seizing a billet of wood from the hearth,
smote him upon the head so shrewdly that the blood
dropped upon the rushes from the wound. When Sir
Raoul knew his wound to be both deep and large no
more he desired to play, so he arose from the floor and
departed straightway from that chamber to his own
lodging, a long mile thence, and sought a surgeon for
his hurt. For her part the faithful lady called upon
Dame Hersent, and returning to her bath, complained
to her of this strange adventure with the knight.

Very great and rich was the feast that the father of the fair lady ordained against the home-coming of Sir Robert. Many a lord was bidden to his hall, and amongst these my lord, Sir Raoul, his knight; but he sent messages that he might not come, for reason of his sickness. On the Sunday came Sir Robert, and was sweetly welcomed of all; but the father of the fair lady sought out Sir Raoul, nor would hold him excused from the feast because of his grievous wound. There-fore he tired his face and his wound the best that he was able, and went to hall, where all day long the lords and ladies sat at meat and drink, and rose for morris and to dance.

When closed the night Sir Robert sought his chamber, and very graciously the lady received him, as it becometh every wife to receive her husband. On the morrow again the guests were gathered about the board, but after dinner uprose Sir Raoul demanding that Messire Robert should pay his wager, since he had had to do with his wife, by sign and token of a certain black spot beneath her right breast.

"Of that I know nothing," answered Sir Robert, "for I have not looked so boldly upon her."

"I require you by the faith that you have pledged me to take heed, and to do me justice herein."

"That will I, truly," answered Sir Robert.

When came the night once more, then Sir Robert observed his wife curiously, and marked the black spot upon her white body, whereat the greater grief was his. In the morning he sought out Sir Raoul, and owned before his lord that he had lost the bet. Sick at heart was he throughout the day. When darkness came he went to the stable, and saddling his palfrey, issued forth from the courtyard, taking with him what he might carry of his wealth. So he set forth on the road to Paris, and coming to the city sojourned therein for some three days. There the tale ceaseth to speak of him, and telleth of his wife.

Very dolent and right heavy was the fair lady that thus her lord had fled his house. Very long and right greatly she considered the reason of his flight. She wept and lamented her widowhood, even till such time as her father entered her chamber, and said that it were much better that she had never wed, since she had brought him to shame, him, and all her house, and told her how and why. When she heard this thing she was sick of heart, and swore that never had she done such deed; but her words profited her nothing, for though a woman gave her body to be burned, yet would none believe her clean of sin, once such blame is set upon her.

Very early in the night the lady rose from the bed, and taking what wealth she had in her coffer, saddled a palfrey and took the road. She had sheared her dainty tresses to the shoulder, and in all points was clad as a boy. In this manner came she to Paris, seeking for her husband, for to her heart she declared that never would she give over her search until they were met together once more. So she rode at adventure, a squire searching for her lord. Now on a morning she departed from Paris, and riding on the way to Orleans came to Tombe Isoire, and there met with Sir Robert, her husband. Her heart was very full as she drew close and saluted him, and he rendered her greeting for greeting, saying—

"Fair friend, God give you heart's desire."

"Sir," said she, "from whence come you?"

"Certes, fair friend, I am of Hainault."

"Sir, and whither go you?"

"Forsooth, fair friend, little I know where my path may lead me, nor have I home where I may dwell. Where Fortune hales me, thither I must go, and the Dame looks not kindly on me, for I have lost the thing that most I loved in all the world, and she hath lost me. Moreover with her went house and lands that were fair and deep. But tell me, what is your name, and whither doth God bring you?"

"Certes, sir," answered Jehane, "I purpose to seek Marseilles, near by the sea, where as I hope there is noise of war. There, if I may, will I enter the service of some hardy captain and learn the trade of arms, so it be God's pleasure. For such is my plight that in no-wise can I stay in my own country. To my eyes, sir, you seem a knight whom I would serve very gladly, if such was your will, nor of my fellowship could you take any harm."

"Fair friend," answered Messire Robert, "truly am I a belted knight, and in what place the battle is set, there would I gladly ride. But tell me now, what is your name?"

"Sir, my name is John."

"It is right welcome," said the knight.

"And you, sir, what is your name?"

"John, my name is Robert."

"Sir Robert, join me to your company as squire, and I will serve you to the utmost of my power."

"John, so would I do gladly, but I have so little

money in my pouch, that ere three days are gone I
must sell my very steed; therefore I may take no
squire."

"Sir," said John, "be not troubled thereat, for God
will provide, if so it seems good to Him. But where
are you set to dine?"

"John, my dinner is a simple business, for I have
nothing in my purse save three sous of Paris."

"Sir, be not troubled thereat, for on my part I have
with me nearly ten pounds of Tournay money, and
these are as your own, since your wallet is not heavy
to your wish."

"Fair friend, thanks, and thanks again."

The two comrades rode at a brisk pace to Montl-
hery, where John found meat for his lord, and they
ate together. When they had eaten they sought their
chamber, the knight lying in a fair bed, and John
sleeping in another, at his feet. Refreshed with sleep,
John rose and did the harness upon their horses, so
they mounted and passed upon their way. Journeying
thus at last they lighted at Marseilles upon the Sea, but
to their grief they might not hear the rumour of any
war. There for the time my story ceases to speak of
the two of them, and returns to Messire Raoul,
that false knight, who, by leasing, had wrongly gained
the land of Sir Robert.

For more than seven years did Messire Raoul hold
the lands of Sir Robert against law and right. Then
a sore sickness took hold upon him, and afflicted him
so grievously that very near he came to death. Much
he feared the wrong he had wrought to that fair lady,
the daughter of his lord, and to her husband besides,
for by reason of his malice were they utterly undone.

So great was his sin that he dared not show the matter to the priest, but tossed upon his bed in utter unrest. On a certain day when his sickness lay too heavy upon him he bade his chaplain draw near his bed, for this priest was a wise confessor, loyal and true, and very close to the sick man's heart. Then he spake—

"Father—my father in God, if not according to the flesh—the time is come when I must die. For God's love give me now your counsel, as you are a ghostly man, for on my soul there lies a sin so ugly and so black that scarcely may I hope to be anealed."

The priest prayed him to speak more plainly, so that he might aid him to the utmost of his power, wherefore Sir Raoul brought himself to tell the story that you have heard. At the end he begged the chaplain for the love of God to show him what he must do to obtain the grace of pardon for a sin so dark.

"Sir," said the priest, "be not altogether cast down, for so you are willing to do such penance as I lay upon you, I will take your sin on me and on my own soul, and you shall be clean."

"Now tell me of this penance," said the knight.

"Sir, within a year of your recovery from this sickness must you take the cross and pass beyond the sea, and in all places where men ask the reason of your pilgrimage, there you must tell the story of this bitter wrong. Moreover, this day must you give hostages to God that thus you will do."

"All this will I do gladly."

"Sir, what rich pledge can you offer, therefor?"

"The best," replied the knight. "You, yourself, shall be hostage and surety for me; and on my honour as a knight well will I redeem my pledge."

"Sir," said the priest, "in the hand of God am I set
as your pledge."

The sick man turned from death to life, and soon
was altogether healed. A full year passed away, and yet
he had not taken the cross. Right often the holy man
reminded him of his bond, but he treated the covenant
as a jest. Then the chaplain told him straitly that
except he discharged him as his surety before God, he
would tell the whole matter to the father of the fair
lady whom he had utterly destroyed. When the knight
heard this he said to the chaplain that within six
months would he seek the sea for the springtide cross-
ing, and thereto he plighted faith. But now the story
ceases to speak of Messire Raoul, and returns to King
Florus of Ausay, of whom it has told nought for a
great while.

A right happy life led King Florus and his wife together, as becomes bride and groom who wed fondly
in their youth, but very dolent and sore of heart were
they that they might get no child. The lady caused
Masses to be sung, and was urgent in prayer for her
desire, but since it was not according to the will of
God, no gain she got thereby. On a day there came to
the castle of King Florus a holy hermit who dwelt
deep within the great forest of Ausay, in a very deso-
late place. The queen received him very gladly, and
because he was a wise man and a holy, would be
shriven by him of her sins. So she bared him her
secret wound, and told him of her grief that she might
have no child by her lord.

"Ah, madame," said the holy man, "it becometh
you patiently to suffer the pleasure of our Lord. When

it is His will, then shall the barren become a joyful mother of children."

"Certes, sir," said the lady, "would that it were now, for less dear am I to my lord therefor. Moreover, the high barons of this realm cast the thing against me, and give counsel to my lord that he should put the barren woman away and take another bride."

"Truly, madame," said the holy man, "grievously would he sin against God and Holy Church by such a deed."

"Ah, sir, pray you to God for me that I may bear a child to my lord, for much I doubt that he will put me away."

"Madame," said the holy man, "prayers of mine are little worth, save by the will of God, yet such as they are you shall have them willingly."

Hardly had this holy man departed from the lady, when the barons of the realm drew together before the King, and counselled him that he should put away his wife, since by her he might have no child, and take another bride. Moreover, if he would not abide by their counsel, then would they withdraw their fealty, for in no case should the kingdom remain without an heir. King Florus feared his barons greatly, and gave credence to their word, so he promised to send his wife to her kindred, and prayed the lords to seek him another queen, which thing was accorded between them. When the lady knew thereof she was stricken to the heart, but nothing might she do, for well she understood that her lord was purposed to forsake her. Therefore she sent to seek that hermit who was her confessor, and when he was come she set before him this business of the barons, and how they would bring another wife to her husband. "So I pray you, fair father, to aid me with counsel as to what I must do."

"Lady," said the holy man, "if it be thus, you must suffer it as best you may, for against king and barons you can make no head."

"Sir," said the gentle lady, "you speak truly; so, if it pleases God, I will dwell as an anchoress near to you, for then shall I serve God all the days of my life, and yet draw some stay and comfort from your presence."

"Lady," said the prudent man, "that were too hazardous a thing, for you are too tender in years, and fair and fresh. But I will tell you what to do. Near by my hermitage is a convent of White Nuns, very quiet and devout. If you go thither, right gladly will they receive you, as well by reason of your blameless life as of your high degree."

"Sir," said she, "wisely have you spoken, and this I will do, since so you counsel me."

On the morrow King Florus spake to his wife, and said—

"Since you may have no child by me, needs must we say farewell. I tell you truly that the parting presses hardly upon me, for never again shall woman lie so nearly to my heart as you have lain."

Then might he speak no more because of tears, and the lady wept with him.

"Husband," said she, "for God's love have pity upon me, for where may I hide myself, and what may I find to do?"

"Wife, so it pleases God, your good days are not yet past, for honourably and in rich estate shall you return to your own friends in your own land."

"Lord," said the dame, "I require none of this gear. So it please you, I will bestow me in a certain convent of nuns, if it will receive me, and there I will serve God all my life; for since I lose your love I am she whose heart shall never harbour love again."

So King Florus and the lady wept together very bitterly.

On the third day the Queen set forth to her convent; and the fresh Queen came to the palace in great pomp, and held revel and festival with her friends. For four years did King Florus possess this lady, yet never might he get an heir. So now the story ceases to speak of King Florus, and turns again to Messire Robert and to John, who were come to Marseilles.

Very sad was Sir Robert when he came to the city that he might hear of no arming in all the land; so he said to John—

"What shall we do? You have lent me much money, for the which I owe you more than thanks. I will give it you again, though I have to sell my very palfrey, to discharge me of the debt."

"Sir," said John, "if it please you give heed to me, and I will show you what we have to do. There remain yet to us one hundred Tournay sous. If you grant me leave, I will turn our two good horses into better money. With this I will make French bread, for I am the lightest baker of whom you have heard, and I doubt but little that we shall gain our money and our livelihood besides."

"John," said Sir Robert, "I am content that you should do according to your will."

The next day John sold his two horses for ten pounds Tournay. With these he bought corn, and car-

ried it to the mill. Afterwards he bought baskets and
set to work at his oven to bake good French bread. So
white and so fresh were these loaves of his baking that
he sold more than the best baker of the town, and
prospered so greatly that within two years he had put
by well one hundred pounds for their need.

Then said John to his lord —

"Would it not be good to hire a fair large house,
with cellarage for wine, that we might offer hostelry
and lodging to wealthy folk from home?"

"John," answered Sir Robert, "your will is mine, for
every reason have I for content with you."

Then John hired a house, both fair and great, and
there gave lodging to honest folk, gaining money very
plenteously. He clad his lord in costly raiment, so that
Sir Robert bestrode his own palfrey, and sat at meat
and drink with the most honourable of the town.
Moreover John caused his board to be furnished with
all manner of wines and store, so that his companions
marvelled greatly at the abundance thereof. With all
this so bravely did John prosper that within four
years he had put by more than three hundred pounds,
besides the furnishing of inn and bakery, which very
well was worth another fifty pounds. But here the story
ceases to speak of John and Sir Robert, and turneth
again to tell of Messire Raoul.

Now telleth the tale that the chaplain pressed Sir
Raoul right earnestly that he should pass beyond the
sea, and thus discharge his surety from the bond, for
much he feared that the knight would yet find reason
to remain. So instant was the priest in pleading, that
Sir Raoul saw well that go he must. He made him
ready for his journey, spending money without stint.

and at the end set forth upon the road, him and his
three squires. He drew presently to Marseilles-on-Sea,
and there sought lodging at the French Hostelry
owned by Sir Robert and by John. When John set eyes
upon him he knew him well, because he had seen him
many times, and for reason of the scar of the wound
that he had given him. The knight sojourned in the
town for fifteen days, till he might find passage in some
vessel going oversea. Whilst he was dwelling at the
inn John took him apart and asked him of the purpose
of his journey, whereat Messire Raoul told him openly all the occasion thereof, just as the tale hath related
already. John listened to his story, but answered
naught for good or evil. Presently Sir Raoul caused his
harness and his gear to be bestowed on the nave, and
mounted in the ship, but for eight days it might not
depart from forth the harbour. On the ninth day the
vessel sailed from port on its way to the Holy Sepul-
chre. Thus Sir Raoul did his pilgrimage, and there
made honest confession of his sins. In sign of penitence his confessor charged him strictly to restore to
the knight and his lady the fief he held in scorn of law
and right; and Sir Raoul promised straitly that when
he came again to his own land he would carry out the
wishes of his heart. So parting from Jerusalem he voyaged to Acre, and took passage in the first homing
ship, as a man who desires above all things to look
upon the face of his own country. He adventured on
the sea, and fared so speedily, by night as by day, that
in less than three months he cast anchor at the port
of Aigues Mortes. Parting from the harbour he stayed
not till he was come to Marseilles, where he rested
eight days at the inn owned by Sir Robert and John,

which inn men called the French Hostelry; but Sir
Robert did not recall him to mind, for he thought but
little of Sir Raoul. At the end of eight days he set
forth from Marseilles with his three squires, and at
length returned to his own home, where his household
received him gladly, for he was a great lord, very rich
in land and in store. His chaplain inquired of him if
any had asked the reason for his journey.

"Yes," said he, "in three places, to wit, Marseilles,
Acre, and Jerusalem. Moreover, that priest who shrived
me counselled me to give back his lands to my lord,
Sir Robert, so I may find him, or if I may not hear of
him, to his wife or his heirs."

"Certes," said the chaplain, "he gave you godly
counsel."

So Messire Raoul dwelt in his own house for a great
while in peace and ease; and there the tale ceaseth to
speak of him, and returns to Messire Robert and to
John.

Sir Robert and John dwelt as citizens in Marseilles
for the space of six years. At the end of six years had
they put by in a sure place the sum of six hundred
pounds. John and his business prospered exceedingly,
for so gentle was he and diligent, that he was beloved
of all his neighbours. Men spake almost too well of
him, and he maintained his lord in such estate and
worship that it was marvellous to see. When the end
of the seventh year drew near, John sought occasion
to speak soberly to Sir Robert his lord, and said—

"Sir, we have dwelt a great while in this city, and
have been so fortunate in our dealings that we have
gained nearly six hundred pounds in money and in
silver vessels."

"Certes," said Sir Robert, "all this, John, is not mine but yours, for you have earned it."

"Sir," said John, "saving your grace, it is not mine, but yours, for you are my own true lord, and never, please God, will I take another."

"John, I thank you heartily," said Robert. "I hold you not as servant, but as comrade and as friend."

"Sir," said John, "all my days have I given you loyal service, and so will I ever do."

"By my faith," said Sir Robert, "what you require of me, that is my pleasure. But as to returning to my own country, I know not what to say. So much have I lost there that never can it be made up to me."

"Sir," answered John, "fret not over your loss, for, so God pleases, you shall hear good news when you come into your own land. And be not fearful of anything, for in whatever place we shall be, please God, I shall gather enough for me and for you."

"Certes, John," said Sir Robert, "I will do that which pleases you, and lodge wheresoe'er you will."

"Sir," said John, "now will I sell our goods and make ready for the journey, for we shall part within fifteen days."

So John sold all the fair furnishing of his houses, and bought thereout three horses, a palfrey for his lord, another for himself, and a pack horse for the road. Then they bade farewell to their neighbours and to the most worshipful citizens of the town, who grieved sorely at their going.

Sir Robert and John travelled so hardily that in less than three weeks they drew to their own country, and Sir Robert caused it to be told to his lord, whose daughter he had wedded, that he was near at hand.

The lord was merry at heart, for much he hoped that his daughter might be with her husband; and so she was, but hid in the trappings of a squire.

The lord greeted Robert warmly, but when he could learn no tidings of his daughter, his mirth was turned into sorrow; nevertheless he made a rich banquet for Sir Robert, and bade his knights and his neighbours to the feast. Amongst these came Sir Raoul who held Sir Robert's land in his despite. Great was the merriment on that day and the morrow, and during all this joy Sir Robert told to John the story of his wager, and of the manner in which Sir Raoul spoiled him of his land.

"Sir," said John, "challenge him to combat as a false traitor, and I will fight the battle in your stead."

"John," said Sir Robert, "this you shall not do."

Thus they left the matter till the morrow, when John came to Sir Robert, and said that he was purposed to speak to the father of his wife. So they sought the lord, and John spake him thus—

"Sir, you are, after God, the lord of my master Sir Robert, who in the years that are gone married your child. As you know, a wager was made between him and Sir Raoul, who said that ere Sir Robert came home from St. James's shrine he would gain the lady to his wish. Sir Raoul spake falsely, and is a most disloyal and traitor knight, for never had he part or share in your daughter's love. All which I am ready to prove upon his body."

Then Robert strode forth and said—

"John, fair friend, this business is mine alone, nor because of it shall you hang shield about your neck."

So Sir Robert held forth his gage to his lord, and

Sir Raoul tendered gage of battle in return, though but fearfully; for needs must he defend himself, or be proclaimed recreant and traitor. Thus were the pledges given, and the day for the ordeal by battle pronounced to be fifteen days thence without appeal.

Now hearken well to this strange story of John, and what he did. John, who more sweetly was named Madame Jehane, had in the house of her father a certain cousin, who was a fair demoiselle of some twenty-five years. To this cousin Jehane went and discovered the whole matter, telling her all the story, from the first thing to the last. She prayed her, moreover, to keep the business hidden, until such time and hour as she should make herself known to her father. The cousin—to whom Jehane was very well known—promised readily to conceal the matter, saying that never should the secret be made plain by her fault. Then was the chamber of her cousin made fresh and ready for Madame Jehane. Therein for the two weeks before the battle Jehan bathed and perfumed her, and took her ease as best she might, for well had she reason to look her fairest. Also she caused women to shape closely to her figure four goodly gowns; one was of scarlet, one of vair, one of peacock blue, and one of trailing silk. Thus with rest and peace she came once more to the fulness of her beauty, and was so dainty, fresh and fair, that no lady showed her peer in all the world.

As for Sir Robert, very greatly was he discomforted during all these fifteen days at the loss of John his squire, for he knew nothing of his fate. Nevertheless on the appointed day he got himself into his harness, and prepared him for the battle stoutly and with a good heart.

On the appointed day the two knights entered within the lists together. Drawing apart for a little space, they rushed furiously the one on the other, and gave such mighty strokes with the blades of their great swords that their horses were borne to the ground beneath them. Sir Raoul was wounded lightly in the left side, so Sir Robert getting first upon his feet came swiftly to him, and smote him with all his force upon the helm. So mighty was the blow that the sword sheared clear through the helmet to the coif of steel, but the coif was so strong that the head was not wounded; nevertheless of that stroke he reeled so that had he not caught at his saddle, certainly he had fallen to the earth. Then Sir Raoul, who was a very stout champion, struck Sir Robert so fiercely upon the head-piece that he was all bemused, and the sword glancing downwards upon the shoulder hacked off the mail of the hauberk, but did him no hurt. Thereat Sir Robert smote him again with all the strength that he was able, and the blow lighting upon the buckler carried away a quarter of the shield. When Sir Raoul knew the hardiness of his foe much he feared for the issue of the combat, and well he wished himself once more beyond the sea, and Sir Robert settled safely on his land. However, he put forward all his prowess, and pressed Sir Robert so grimly that with one great stroke he clove to the boss upon the very middle of Sir Robert's shield. For his part Sir Robert struck fairly at Sir Raoul's helm, but he thrust his shield before him, and that mighty blow passing clean through the buckler came full upon the charger's neck, so that horse and rider tumbled to the ground. Messire Raoul climbed stoutly to his feet, as a valiant man who had often

ridden with the spears, but Sir Robert lighted from
his steed, for he would not deign to fight at vantage
with a foe on foot.

Now strove the two knights together, hand to
hand, in such fashion that shield and helm and hauberk were hewn in pieces, and the blood ran from
their bodies by reason of their trenchant glaives. Had
they been able to deal such blows as in the first passage of their arms, very quickly both one and the other
had been slain, for of their shields scarce enough held
together to cover their gauntlets. The fear of death or
shame was now before their eyes, and the nearness of
their persons summoned them to bring this judgment
to an end. Sir Robert gripped his sword in both hands,
and with all the greatness of his strength smote Sir
Raoul upon the helm. Half the shattered headpiece
fell upon his shoulders, and the sword cutting through
the coif made a grisly wound. So bewildered was Sir
Raoul at the stroke that he was beaten to the knee;
but he rose lightly again, though, since he knew that
his head was naked, very fearful was he of death. He
ran therefore at Sir Robert, smiting with all his power
at the remnants of his shield. Through shield and helmet went the glaive to the depth of full three fingers,
but the wearied sword coming full upon the coif of
steel brake in pieces, for the armourer's work was very
strong. When Sir Raoul looked upon the shards of his
sword, and remembered that his head was naked,
much he doubted of his end. Nevertheless he stooped
to the ground, and seizing a great stone in both his
hands flung it at Sir Robert with all his might. Sir
Robert stepped aside quickly, avoiding the cast, and
ran in upon his adversary, who turned his back and

took to flight about the lists. So Sir Robert cried that save his foe admitted himself recreant and shamed he would slay him with the sword.

"Gentle knight," answered Sir Raoul, "I yield thee what remaineth of my sword, and throw myself entirely on thy grace. Show mercy on me, gentle knight, and pray thy lord and mine that he have pity upon me, and spare my life. Take back thy land that I have held against both law and right, and therewith take my own; for all I said against that fair and spotless lady was just foul lies."

When my lord, Sir Robert, heard these words he thought within himself that Sir Raoul might do no more. Therefore he prayed his lord so urgently to pardon Sir Raoul for this felony, that his prayer was accorded on such terms that Sir Raoul should abide over sea for all his days.

In such fashion Sir Robert won back his land, and added that of Sir Raoul besides. But in this thing he found little comfort, for grief of heart over the fair and faithful lady from whom he had parted. Moreover, in no wise could he forget John, his squire, who was lost to him also. His lord, too, shared in his sorrow, for reason that he might never gain tidings of his one fair child.

But Madame Jehane, who had spent two weeks in her cousin's chamber in all ease and comfort, when she heard that her husband had gained the battle, was greatly content. As we know, she had caused her women to shape closely to her person four goodly gowns, and of these she arrayed herself in the most rich, which was of cloth of silk, banded with fine Arabian gold. So shapely was she of body, so bright of face, and

so gracious of address that nothing more lovely could
be found in all the world, so that her very cousin, even, marvelled at her exceeding beauty. For the
bathing, the tiring, and ease of mind and body of the
past fifteen days had given her back her early fresh-
ness, as was wonderful to see. Very sweet, very ravish-
ing showed Madame Jehane in her silken robe banded
with gold. So when she was ready she called to her
cousin, and said—

"How seem I to thee?"

"Why, dame, the prettiest person in all the world."

"Now, fair cousin, I will tell thee what thou shalt
do. Go thou straight to my father, and tell him to be
heavy no more, but rather merry and glad, because
thou bringest him good news of his daughter. Tell him
that she is sound and well, and that so he come with
thee, he shall see her with his eyes. Then lead him
here, and he will greet me again, I deem, right willingly."

The maiden answered that gladly would she give
the message, so she sought out the father of Madame
Jehane, and said as she was bidden. When the lord
heard thereof he wondered at this strange thing, and
going after the damsel found his daughter in her
chamber. When he saw her face he cast his arms about
her neck, shedding tears of joy and pity, yea, such was
his happiness that scarcely could he find a word. When
he might speak he asked where she had been so long
a while.

"Fair father," said the lady, "you shall hear it in
good time. But, for the love of God, cause my mother
to come to me speedily, for I die till I see her once
again."

The lord sent incontinent for his wife, and when she was come into the chamber where her daughter lay, and saw and knew her face, straight she fell down in a swoon for joy, and might not speak for a great space. But when her senses were come to her again no man could conceive the joy and festival she made above her child.

Whilst mother and daughter held each other fast, the father of the fair lady went in quest of Sir Robert, and meeting him said thus—

"Fair sweet son, very joyful news have I to share with you."

"Certes," said Sir Robert, "of joy have I great need, but God alone can help my evil case, for sad at heart am I for the loss of my sweet wife, and sad, besides, for the loss of him who did me more good than any other in the world, for John, my faithful squire."

"Sir Robert," said the lord, "spoil not your life for John; squires can be met with at every turning. But as to your wife, I have a certain thing to tell, for I come from her but now, and know well that she is the most peerless lady in all the world."

When Messire Robert heard this he fell a-trembling with joy, and said to his lord—

"Ah, sir, for God's love bring me to see that this is true!"

"Right willingly," said the lord, "come now with me."

The lord went before and Robert followed after, till they were come to the chamber where mother and daughter yet clasped each other close, weeping with joy the one upon the other. When they knew their husbands near they drew apart, and as soon as Sir

Robert saw his wife he ran to her with open arms, and embraced her. So they kissed each the other with many little kisses, and wept for joy and pity. Yea, they held each to the other in this fashion whilst a man might run ten acres of land, nor ceased enlacing. Then the lord commanded that the tables should be spread for supper; so they ate with mirth and merriment.

After supper, when the songs and the dances were done, they went to their beds, neither was Sir Robert parted from the lady Jehane, for they were right happy to be met together again, and talked of many things. At the last Sir Robert asked of her where she had been so great a time, and she said—

"Husband, it is overlong a story to tell, but you shall hear it all at a more convenient season. Tell me, rather, what you have done, and where you have been all this while."

"Wife," said Sir Robert, "I will tell you gladly."

So he told her all the tale she knew by rote, and of John his squire, who gained him bread, and said that so distressed was he at the loss of his companion that never would he give over the search till he had found him, yea, that he would saddle with the morn and part.

"Husband," said the lady, "that would be madness. Are you set again to leave me, and what shall I do thereof?"

"Certes, lady, I can do none other; for never man did such things for his friend as he has done for me."

"Husband," said the wife, "what he did for you was but his duty; he did no more than what he should have done."

"Wife," said Messire Robert, "by your speech you should have known him."

"Truly," answered the lady, "truly, I should know him well, for never aught of what he did was hid from me."

"Lady," said Sir Robert, "I marvel at such words."

"Sir," said she, "there is no need for wonder. If I tell you, yea and verily, that such a thing is true, will you honestly believe my word?"

"Wife," said he, "on my honour."

"Believe, then, what I am about to tell you, for know assuredly that I am that very John whom you would seek, and this is how it happed. When I was told the matter of the wager, and of the treason of Messire Raoul; when, too, I knew that you were fled because of your grief at my faithlessness, and by reason of the land that for ever you had lost, then was I more cast down than any woman since woman first was made. So I clipped my hair close to my head, and taking all the money in my chest, about ten pounds Tournay, I arrayed me in the guise of a squire, and followed after you to Paris, coming up with you at Tombe Isoire. From there we companied together, even to Marseilles, where I served you as my own liege lord for near seven years, nor do I grudge you varlet's service. And know for truth that I am innocent and clean of that deed the foul knight fastened upon me, as clearly now appears, for he has been put to shame in open field, and has publicly confessed his treason."

Having spoken thus, Madame Jehane embraced Sir Robert, her lord, and kissed him very sweetly on the mouth. When Messire Robert was persuaded that she, indeed, was John, his faithful squire, his joy was greater far than thought or words may express, and much he marvelled that so high a lady could prove so lowly and so serviceable. For which thing he loved her the more dearly all the days of his life.

Thus came together these two parted lovers; thus, on their own domain, which was both broad and fair, they lived a happy life, as becometh lovers in their youth. Often Sir Robert rode to tournaments in the train of his lord, and much honour he gained and such wealth, moreover, that his land became twice as great as that he had. After the death of the father and mother of Lady Jehane he became the heir to all their substance. So stout a knight was he, that by his prowess he was made a double banneret, and was worth four thousand pounds in land. Yet always must he be a childless man, to his exceeding grief, though for more than ten years he was with his wife after the combat with Sir Raoul.

After the term of ten years, by the will of God—which is mightier than the strength of man—the pains of death gat hold upon him. He met death like a brave knight, assoiled by the rites of Holy Church, and was laid in his grave with great honour. His wife, the fair lady, mourned so grievously upon him, that all about her felt pity for her sorrow. Yet, during the days, the sharpness of her grief was assuaged, and she came to take a little comfort, though as yet it was but a little.

The Lady Jehane bore herself during her widowhood as a devout and kindly lady, devoted to God and Holy Church. Very humble was she and right charitable, dearly cherishing the poor and needy. So good was she that no tongue might say aught of her but praise; and so fair that all who looked upon her owned that she was the mirror of all ladies in the world for beauty and for virtue. But now for a little space the tale ceases to speak of her, and returns to tell of King Florus, for it has been dumb of him o'erlong.

King Florus of Ausay lay at his own castle sorely grieved and vexed at the departure of his first wife, for she whom the barons had seated in her chair, though fresh and gracious, might not bring that peace of heart which was that lady's gift. Four years they lived together, yet never might have an heir. At the end thereof the pains of death seized the lady, so she was buried amidst the weeping of her friends, and with such fair state and service as were fitting to the dignity of a queen.

King Florus remained a widower for above two years. He was yet a young man, for he was no more than forty-five years of age, and his barons prayed him that he would seek another wife.

"Certes," answered King Florus, "I desire not greatly to do this thing, for I have had two wives, yet might not get an heir by either. Moreover, the first wife that I had was so virtuous and so fair, and so dearly did I love her in my heart for her exceeding goodlihead, that never is she absent from my thoughts. I tell you truly that never again will I wed till I may meet a woman sweet and good as she. God rest her soul, for as I hear she passed away in that White convent where she was withdrawn."

"Ah, sire," said a knight who was in his private counsel, "many a comely dame goes about the realm whom you have never seen. One at least I know who for kindness and for beauty has not her like in all the world. If you but saw her fairness, if you but knew her worth, you would own that fortunate indeed were he—yea, though a king—who might own such rich treasure. She is a gentlewoman, discreet, and rich in money and in lands, and, if you will, I can tell you many a tale of her discretion and of her worth."

The King replied that gladly would he hear; so the knight related how the lady set out to follow after her lord, how she came up with him and brought him to Marseilles, and the many kindnesses and the great services she rendered him, just as the tale hath told before. Thereat King Florus marvelled much, and said privily to the knight that very gladly would he become the husband of such a wife.

"Sire," answered the knight, who was near neighbour to Madame Jehane, "I will seek the lady, if such is your good pleasure, and will speak her so fairly, if I may, that in marriage you twain may be one."

"Yea," said King Florus, "get you speedily to horse, and I pray you to be diligent in your embassy."

The knight passed straightway upon his errand, and without any tarrying came to the land where dwelt that lovely lady whom the tale calls Madame Jehane. He found her in a certain castle of hers, and she welcomed him gladly as a neighbour and a friend. When they might have some private speech together, the knight conveyed to her the commandment of King Florus, that she should ride to him and be wedded as his wife. When the lady heard his word she smiled more sweetly than ever siren sang, and answered softly to the knight—

"Your king knows less of women, nor is he so courteous, as fame has bruited, to command that I should hasten to him that he may take me as his wife. Certes,

I am not a handmaid to ride to him for wages. But tell your king rather to come to me if he finds my love so desirable and sweet, and woo me to receive him as husband and as spouse. For truly the lord should pray and require the lady, and not the lady the lord."

"Lady," answered the knight, "all that you have told me will I tell him again; but I doubt that he will come for pride."

"Sir knight," said the lady, "he will do the thing that pleases him; but in this matter he shows neither courtesy nor reason."

"Lady," said the knight, "in God's name, so let it be. With leave I take farewell to seek my lord the King, and will tell him as I am bidden. So if there is any over-word give it me before I part."

"Yea," said the lady. "Take to him my greeting, and add my fairest thanks for the honour to which he calls me."

The knight parted from the lady forthwith, and on the fourth day returned to King Florus of Ausay, whom he found in his chamber, deep in business with his privy council. The knight saluted the King, who gave him his salutation again, and seating him by his side, asked how it chanced in this matter of the lady. Then the knight gave the message with which she charged him; how she would not come, for she was no kitchen-maid to haste at his bidding for her wages; but that rather should a lord pray and require of a lady; how that she sent him her fairest greeting, and her sweetest thanks for the honour he craved of her.

When King Florus heard these words, he pondered in his seat, nor did any man speak for a great space.

"Sire," said a knight, who was of his inmost mind,

"what do you consider so deeply? Certes, all these words most richly become a discreet and virtuous lady, and—so help me God—she is both wise and brave. In good faith you will do well to fix upon a day when you can seek her, and send her greetings and letters that on such a day you will arrive to do her honour, and to crave her as your bride."

"Certes," said King Florus, "I will send her letters that I will lie at her castle for Easter, and that she make all ready to receive her husband and her King."

Then King Florus bade the knight who was his messenger to prepare himself within three days to carry these tidings to his lady. On the third day the knight set forth, and, riding hard, brought messages to the lady that the King would spend Easter at her castle. So she answered that since it was God's will it was woman's too, and that she would take counsel with her friends, and would array herself to receive him as the honour of a lady and his greatness required. At these words the knight returned to his lord, King Florus, and gave him the answer of the fair lady as you have heard. So King Florus of Ausay made him ready for his journey, and with a great company set forth to the country of this fair dame. When he was come there he took and married her with great pomp and festival. Then he brought her to his own realm, where she was welcomed of all most gladly. And King Florus joyed exceedingly over his wife because of her great beauty, and because of the right judgment and high courage that were in her.

Within the year that the King had taken her to wife the fair Jehane was delivered of a daughter, and afterwards she rejoiced as the mother of a son. The boy was named Florence, and the girl Flora. The boy Florence was very goodly to see, and after he was made knight was esteemed the hardiest warrior of his day, insomuch that he was chosen to be Emperor of Constantinople. A mighty prince was he, and wrought great mischief and evil to the Paynims. As to the Princess Flora, she became the Queen of her father's realm, and the son of the King of Hungary took her as wife, so was she lady of two kingdoms.

Such honour as this God gave to the fair lady because of her true and loyal heart. For many years King Florus lived happily with his virtuous wife, and when it was the will of God that his days should end, he took back to his Maker a stainless soul. The lady endured to live but six months after him, and departed from this world as became so good and loyal a dame with a quiet mind.

Here finishes the tale of King Florus and the fair Jehane.

OF THE COVETOUS MAN AND OF
THE ENVIOUS MAN

ONCE upon a time, more than one hundred years ago, there lived two companions, who spent their days together very evilly. The one of these comrades was so brimmed with envy, that you might find no heart so rank with the gall of bitterness. The other was so filled with covetousness, that nothing sufficed of all that could be given to him. Now covetousness is so foul a vice, that often she bringeth many men to shame. Covetousness lendeth out her money upon usury, and deceiveth with her balances, so that he who lendeth may have the greater gain. But envy is the worser sin, since she grudges joy to others, and is desirous of all the wealth of all the world.

On a day the envious man and the covetous man were about their business together, and they came upon St. Martin walking in the fields. But the saint had been but a little space in their company when he perceived very clearly the evil desires that were rooted in the hidden places of their hearts. Thus they fared till they lighted on two beaten paths, one going this way, and the other that, and a chapel stood between the ways. There St. Martin stayed his steps, and beckoned to these evil-minded men.

"Lords," said he, "I take this path to the right that I may enter within the church. I am St. Martin, who bestowed his cloak on the beggar, and that you may always keep in mind this meeting I will give, in turn, to each of you a gift. He who makes known to me his prayer shall have his desire granted forthwith. But to him who refrains from words, straightway shall be given twice as much as is bestowed upon his fellow."

So when St. Martin was gone, the covetous man considered within himself that if he left his companion to require a gift, he would receive twice as much as him, and sweetly enjoy a double gain.

"Make your prayer, fair fellow, to the holy saint," said he, "for very surely you will receive of him all that you may ask. Ask largely of him, for he will largely give. If you go prudently about the matter you will be wealthy all your life."

But he whose heart was brimmed with venom and envy dared not to ask according to his desire, for reason that he feared to die of grief and malice that his comrade's portion should be larger than his. Thus for a great while they kept their tongues from speech, turning the business over, this way and that.

"Wait no longer, lest a mischief befall you," cried at last the covetous man. "Yea you or nay you, I must have the double of your share, for all your cunning and caution. Ask, or I will beat you more grievously than ever yet was beaten donkey at Pont."

"Sire," answered the envious man, "pray I will, since it is better to receive a gift than stripes. If I require of the saint, money or houses or lands, very surely will you receive of his bounty twice that he giveth to me. But, so I am able, of all these shall you get nothing. Holy St. Martin, I pray and require of your clemency that I may lose one of my eyes, so that my fellow may lose both of his; thus shall he be pained and grieved in double measure."

Very careful was the saint to observe his covenant, and of four eyes these comrades lost three, since the envious man became one-eyed, and the covetous man a poor blind beggar. Thus these fair friends were ruined by their gain. But sorrow may he have who lets his heart be troubled by their wretched plight, for these men were not of sterling gold, but of false alloy.

OF A JEW WHO TOOK AS SURETY
THE IMAGE OF OUR LADY

SO many marvels are written of the sweet miracles of
Our Lady, that amongst them I scarce know which to
choose. Yet, alas! I have not that long leisure to set
them forth before you every one. Then must it be
with me as with him who walks abroad through summer meadows deep in flowers. Before, behind, on
either side, he sees the countless blossoms of the field.
Blue, vermeil, gold, they dance upon the green. Then,
since he may not gather all, he plucks a rose, a lily,
here and there, as he may find them to his hand. So
from amongst the number of Our Lady's lovely deeds
I pluck a leaf, one here, one there, and wreathe this
artless garland, lest I have naught to cast before her
feet.

In days long past—as the scribe hath truly written
—there lived in the strong city of Byzantium a certain
citizen, who held Our Lady very dear. Rich he was,
and of great worship, because of his wealth and of the
praise of men. To keep his station in the eyes of his
fellows, he spent his substance so largely, and thereto
so wantonly, that in a little while he had wasted all
his goods, and naught remained to do but that he
must sell his very lands. Yet so rich of heart was this
burgess that not poverty even might make him knot
his purse. He still kept open house, and gave goodly
cheer to all, ever borrowing more and more, spending
and vending, wasting and hasting to scatter everything
he had. For of poverty he had neither heed nor fear,
so long as he might find a man to lend. But at the

last he was utterly undone. All his friends passed him by when they saw how deeply he was sunk in debt, and that to no lender did he e'er repay what he owed. For he who borrows, never paying back again, neither seeking from others that which is his due, very quickly loses his credit, yea, though he be the King of France.

The good citizen was sore vexed, and knew not what to do or say, when he found that his creditors pressed him hardly, and that he was wholly disappointed of those friends in whom he put his trust. Sore was his sorrow, deep his distress, and bitter his shame, his wrath and sadness, when by no means whatever might he grant his customary bounty, nor of his charity give alms and benefits to the poor. So long as he was a man of worship, with store of gold and silver, great were his doles to those of low estate. But such was the malice wherewith Dame Fortune pursued him, and such the shame and loss she set upon him, that he had nothing left to give to others, or to keep for himself. And since Dame Fortune looked upon him with a frowning countenance, there was none to welcome him with a smiling face.

Now this unhappy burgess knew not what to do, for some of his acquaintance gazed the other way, whilst men, to whom he had done naught but good, jested upon him openly in the street. Doubtless such is the way of the world to those honest folk who are cast beneath at the turn of Fortune's wheel. Therefore those to whom he had shown the greatest kindness requited him with the utmost despite, counting him viler than a dog; and those, who in his day of prosperity loved and affected his company, were the very men who now mocked and despised him. Well say the

Scriptures, Put not your trust in man. For in these days faith is so rare and so forgetful, that the son fails the father in his peril, and the mother may not count upon her maid. Mad is he who strips himself for others, for so soon as he comes before them naked, then they cry, "Beggar, begone!"

When this citizen, who for so long a while had known such great honour, saw himself so scorned, and found that in all the town he had neither kinsman nor friend, he knew not what to say or do, nor whom to take for counsel in his need. So, by the will of God, he turned in his despair to a certain Jew, the richest in all the city. Him he sought out straightway, with a face aflame, and said—

"Master Jew, here is my case. All my daughters, all my sons, all my friends, and, very surely, all of those to whom I have done most good in this world, have failed me utterly and every one. I am stripped of all my substance. Foolish have I been, and unlucky, since I wasted all I had on those very clerks and laymen who desert me now. I am a merchant of great knowledge, and so you will lend me of your treasure, I count to gain so largely, that never shall I have to pray another for a loan; for of your wealth will I make such usage that all will think the more of me thereby."

"Because you have dealt so generously with others," answered the Jew, "in this very hour will I lend you freely of my moneys if you can give me pledge or surety for them."

But the Christian made answer to him—

"Fair, sweet friend, all my kinsfolk and acquaintance have cast me utterly behind them, neither care they for me any more, notwithstanding that they thrive by reason of my gifts and toil. I can offer no kinsman as surety, nor have I a friend in the world. But though I can give neither pledge nor surety, strive how I may, yet I swear to you now on my faith and conscience, that, without fail, I will repay you your loan and your substance on the very day that the debt becomes due."

"If things are thus, I can lend you nothing," answered the Jew; "for grievously I doubt that you may not carry out your bargain."

"Fair, sweet friend," he made reply, "since then I neither have, nor think to have, a pledge to offer, take now in pledge, I pray you, my Maker, in whom is all my faith, this Jesus Christ, the King of Heaven, the King of kings, the God of gods. If you have not your money returned on the very day that you shall name, I swear to you by God, fair brother Jew, and by His Mother, so tender and so dear, that I will become your villein and your serf, in such wise and fashion as any other slave of yours; so that with a ring about my neck you may sell me in the market-place, just as any brute beast."

Now in his heart the Jew greatly desired and longed to make this Christian his bondsman Therefore, laughing, he replied—

"I believe but little that Jesus Christ, the son of Mary, whom our forefathers crucified on a cross of wood, was truly God. But inasmuch as He was doubtless a holy man, and a prophet of mighty name, if you will put Him in pledge in such manner that you will serve me all your life should you fail me in this

our bargain, why, I will take your pledge without
demur."

"Fairly have you spoken," said he, "by my soul. Let
us go straightway to the church of Our Lady, the most
glorious Mother of God."

A great company of Christians and of Jews went
with them to the church, and many a clerk and layman was witness to their device and covenant. Without any delay, the wretched merchant kneeled him
down before the Statue, whilst the hot tears rushed to
his eyes, and over-ran and wetted all his face, because
of the poverty which drove him to this deed. The unhappy man knew not what to do in his plight, but he
cast his burden upon the Lord, and, weeping, prayed
God's precious Mother that she would deign to set
wretchedness and bondage far from him. But very
fearful was he, and sore adread in his heart.

When he had prayed his prayer to Our Lady, he
sprang lightly to his feet, and said—

"Friend Jew, by my soul see here my Surety. In
giving you this Child and this Image, I give you Jesus
Christ, Himself, as pledge. He created me, and He
fashioned me. 'Tis He Who is my bond for your moneys. A richer pledge you may not think to have, so
help me God, now and for evermore."

He placed the hand of the Child in that of the
Jew, and forthwith delivered the pledge and plighted
faith. Then, yet upon his knees, most pitifully, with
eyes all wet, he cried aloud in the hearing of Christian
and of Jew—

"Fair Lord God, most merciful, most mighty and
most sure, at the end of this business, I beseech Thee

with clasped hands, fair, kindest Father, that by the pleadings of Thy sweet Mother, if it should happen that on the appointed day for any cause I may not give again the wealth I owe the Jew, then of Thy courtesy pay Thou my debt, and without an hour's delay redeem Thy pledge and faith. For if but one single day I fail to keep faith, then his serf must I be all the days of my life, save only that I break my oath sworn on this Image."

He rose lightly to his feet, though with a tearful face, and the Jew straightway counted out to him a great sum of money, to deal with in the future as he had dealt with his own. But he had lost the desire to play, for he remembered too plainly that of such mirth comes bitterness. The scalded man hates boiling water, and well he knew, and clearly he perceived, that he who is in rags goes shivering in the wind.

The honest merchant—whom God kept in charge—went forth with a light heart, that leaped and fluttered in his breast, because of the wealth he had in seisin. He bargained for a bark that lay in harbour, and since he had much skill in such business, he stored the ship with divers kinds of merchandise. Then putting his trust in God, and commending body and goods to His keeping, he hoisted sail, and set forth upon the water. He voyaged to divers lands, and trafficked with the merchants thereof to such purpose, that before the year had gone by he was no more in dread of beggary. God increased his store, so that he prospered in every market. But the gains and riches of the merchant in nowise made him grudging of his substance. Freely was given to him, freely he gave to others, for the love of God Who for every man ripens His harvest.

In a short while the merchant became very rich. One market opened another market, and money made more money. So greatly did his substance multiply that at the end, the story tells us, he might not keep the count of his wealth. So to set field by field, and house by house, he travelled in many strange lands. One day darkened, and the next day dawned, but he never gave thought to that certain day when he must return to the Jew the loan of which he had made so fruitful a use. He called it not to mind until there was but one single day between him and the appointed time, and as it chanced he bethought him thereof when he was at sea. He well-nigh swooned when the day came to his heart and memory.

"Ah, gentle Lady of the King of Glory! sweet Maid and debonair!" cried he; "unhappy wretch, what can I do?"

So sore was his grief that with clenched hands he beat upon his breast, and presently with locked teeth fell fainting to the deck, where he lay senseless for a great space. The sailors ran to his succour, and, pressing about him, cried out and lamented his evil case, for certainly they deemed that he was dead. Passing heavy were they at this sad mischance, for not one word could they draw from his lips, nor for all their pains might they find in him either pulse or breath. When he was returned a little from his swoon, he addressed himself to prayer, weeping and sighing for a great while, because for grief he found no words to say.

"Alas!" cried he, "alas, my luckless lot! What a besotted merchant have I been! How foully has misfortune stolen upon me! How has the Adversary beguiled

me, and snared my thoughts, that I might not better
mark the appointed day! Surely on the tables of my
h art should it have been written that for pledge I
gave Jesus Christ, and His Mother, sweet and dear.
Alas! very right is it that I should go heavy, and that
my h art should be sick and sad, since never by day
nor by night have I taken thought how to return that
mighty debt which so affrights me now. Affrighted,
alas! much cause have I to fear. Were a bird now to
quit th ship, yet should he not wing to Byzantium in
thirty lays—no, nor in forty. Foul fall the day, for I
am quite undone. Alas! for the shame I have brought
upon my kin. Very great riches are very little worth,
since thus am I snared and taken."

In this manner the good merchant made his complaint, and with many sighs bewailed his wretched
plight. But when he had eased his heart with words,
the Holy Spirit wrought upon him, so that his courage
came to him again, and he said—

"What is here for tears? Rather should I take comfort in that He, Who hath power over all, is holden as
my pledge. Let me place the matter in his mighty
hand, nor concern myself overmuch with what is His
business more than mine. I owe the money, but He
will pay my debt; and thus by his balm shall I be
healed. On the morrow must I repay the money that
I owe, but there is yet a full night before the money
need be counted to the Jew. I will not concern myself
greatly with this matter, but commend myself humbly
to His will. No other thing is there to do, for none
can deliver me from my trouble, save Him alone. He
is my Surety, and very surely will He discharge me

from this debt, for without Him there is no redemption."

Then straightway the merchant took a strong, clamped coffer, and sealed within it the debt which he must now restore the Jew. Without waiting for the morrow, he cast it into the sea with his own hand, and with tears commended it to that great Lord and God who holds every man in His good keeping, and to Whom earth and sea are ministers and servants alike. So He Who is of such high and puissant majesty, that naught He wills to do is burdensome or heavy to Him, was pleased to steer that coffer with its precious load of besants through the waters, so that it made more than a thousand leagues in that one night. Thus with the dawn it drew right to Byzantium, and on the appointed day the casket and the treasure came to the shore.

Now by the will of God it chanced that the rich Jew, who lent the Christian of his monies, lived in a fair dwelling near by the sea. A certain servant of his rose early from his bed to walk on the shore in the cool summer dawn, and spied the casket, which had but just drawn to land. So, without taking off his raiment, he sprang into the sea that he might lay hold upon it; but he was not able, for the coffer tossed grievously whenever he would make it his own. Very covetous was the varlet of this coffer, yet might he never set his hand upon it. For the casket moved warily, as though it would say, "Go your road, since in nowise am I yours."

So presently the servant sought his lord, and returned with him to the shore. And forthwith the coffer

drew to the very feet of the Jew, and seemed to him
to say—

"Fair Sir Jew, receive your own. By me God re-
deems the merchant from his debt, and henceforth he
is free, quite free of you."

Then the Jew entered swiftly within his door, bearing the casket with him, and when he had counted
over its great riches, he hid the treasure in a privy
place at the foot of his bed, so that none might know
of the matter. Moreover, he found within a certain
letter news that, very soon, this merchant, who so far
had voyaged in so many lands, would seek Byzantium
in ships laden with tissues and broideries and all manner of stuffs and merchandise. So the friends and acquaintance of the merchant rejoiced greatly at his
prosperity, and the whole city welcomed him with
mirth and festival. All men made much of his home-
coming, and clerk and layman joined alike in the
feast.

When the Jew heard the noise of the joyous greeting vouchsafed to the citizen, he rose up quickly, and
sought him out without delay. They spoke at great
length together, and many words passed between the
twain. At the last the Jew made mention of his money,
as if he sought to know when payment should be
made. For presently in his merry talk, yet laughing, he
took the Christian by the hand, and wagging his head
from side to side, said—

"Oh, faithful Christian! oh, faithful Christian!"

Thereat the burgess began to smile, and made reply
that he would learn the meaning of those words.

"By the Law, it means that I have lent you monies
in heaped-up measure from my wealth, to be repaid

me on a day now gone. Since you have failed in bond and faith, now holds the bargain, that should you break your covenant, though but for one single day, then all the years of your life must you labour as my serf. If now you throw me back your bond, then I must reckon your Holy Faith and your plighted word as worth just two grains of dust upon a balance."

Then he, whose only hope was in God, made answer to the Jew, and said—

"I owe you nothing, since all that was your due has been paid to the uttermost doit."

Very cunning was this Jew; therefore he replied—

"Many an honest man was witness to the loan, but what witness can you bring to the payment of the debt? There is little new in such a plea as yours."

"Right easily can I find proof of quittance, and to spare. All this would make me fear, indeed, were not such a mighty Surety at my side. But so you will come with me to the church, where my pledge was taken, very surely will I show you proof of the redemption of my bond."

So they, and a great company with them, went to the minister, which was filled altogether with the press.

Then the citizen, hoping all things of his God, and rooted deeply in his trust, bowed himself down with clasped hands right humbly to the floor before the Image of Our Lady. From his very heart, with all his soul, he prayed and required of her that she would obtain of her sweet Son to hearken to his prayer, and his words were broken by his sighs. Afterwards he cried with a clear voice in the hearing of them all, and said—

"Lord Jesus, so truly as Thou art the very Son of God, witness for me to this Hebrew of the truth as it is known to Thee. Very God of Very God, exalt now Thine honour, and for the glory of Thy Name make clear whether I have discharged me of this debt or not."

Then the Image made answer in these very words—

"It is a true testimony that to the appointed day this Jew has been paid in full whatsoever you have had of him. In proof whereof the casket yet remains hid in a privy place beneath his bed, from whence he took the debt I paid him in your place."

When the Jew heard this marvel he was filled with confusion, and was greatly astonied, so that he knew not what to say, nor what to do. So by the grace and lovingkindness of the Holy Spirit that very day he was baptized, and became a christened man, nor did he ever after waver in that faith.

So every year it was the gracious custom of all good citizens to keep this wonder in remembrance with dances and midnight revelry, with feast and high solemnity. And this holy day was observed in Byzantium, the mighty city, which Constantine, the noble Emperor, afterwards called Constantinople.

THE LAY OF GRAELENT

NOW will I tell you the adventure of Graelent, even as it was told to me, for the lay is sweet to hear, and the tune thereof lovely to bear in mind.

Graelent was born in Brittany of a gentle and noble house, very comely of person and very frank of heart. The King who held Brittany in that day made mortal war upon his neighbours, and commanded his vassals to take arms in his quarrel. Amongst these came Graelent, whom the King welcomed gladly, and since he was a wise and hardy knight, greatly was he honoured and cherished by the Court. So Graelent strove valiantly at tourney and at joust, and pained himself mightily to do the enemy all the mischief that he was able. The Queen heard tell the prowess of her knight, and loved him in her heart for reason of his feats of arms and of the good men spake of him. So she called her chamberlain apart, and said—

"Tell me truly, hast thou not often heard speak of that fair knight, Sir Graelent, whose praise is in all men's mouths?"

"Lady," answered the chamberlain, "I know him for a courteous gentleman, well spoken of by all."

"I would he were my friend," replied the lady, "for I am in much unrest because of him. Go thou and bid him come to me, so he would be worthy of my love."

"Passing gracious and rich is your gift, lady, and

doubtless he will receive it with marvellous joy Why, from here to Troy there is no priest even, however holy, who in looking on your face would not lose Heaven in your eyes."

Thereupon the chamberlain took leave of the Queen, and seeking Graelent within his lodging, saluted him courteously, and gave him the message, praying him to come without delay to the palace.

"Go before, fair friend," answered the knight, "for I will follow you at once."

So when the chamberlain was gone, Graelent caused his grey horse to be saddled, and mounting thereon, rode to the castle, attended by his squire. He descended without the hall, and passing before the King, entered within the Queen's chamber. When the lady saw him she embraced him closely, and cherished and honoured him sweetly. Then she made the knight to be seated on a fair carpet, and to his face praised him for his exceeding comeliness. But he answered her very simply and courteously, saying nothing but what was seemly to be said. Then the Queen kept silence for a great while, considering whether she should require him to love her for the love of love; but at the last, made bold by passion, she asked if his heart was set on any maid or dame.

"Lady," said he, "I love no woman, for love is a serious business, not a jest. Out of five hundred who speak glibly of love, not one can spell the first letter of his name. With such it is idleness, or fulness of bread, or fancy, masking in the guise of love. Love requires of his servants chastity in thought, in word and in deed. If one of two lovers is loyal, and the other jealous and false, how may their friendship last, for love is slain! But sweetly and discreetly love passes from person to person, from heart to heart, or it is nothing worth. For what the lover would, that would the beloved; what she would ask of him, that should he go before to grant. Without accord such as this, love is but a bond and a constraint. For above all things love means sweetness, and truth, and measure; yea, loyalty to the loved one and to your word. And because of this I dare not meddle with so high a matter."

The Queen heard Graelent gladly, finding him so tripping of tongue, and since his words were wise and courteous, at the end she discovered to him her heart.

"Friend, Sir Graelent, though I am a wife, yet have I never loved my lord. But I love you very dearly, and what I have asked of you, will you not go before to grant?"

"Lady," said he, "give me pity and forgiveness, but this may not be. I am the vassal of the King, and on my knees have pledged him loyalty and faith, and sworn to defend his life and honour. Never shall he have shame because of me."

With these words Sir Graelent took his leave of the Queen, and went his way.

Seeing him go in this fashion, the Queen commenced to sigh. She was grieved in her very heart, and knew not what to do. But whatever chanced she would not renounce her passion, so often she required his love by means of soft messages and costly gifts, but he refused them all. Then the Queen turned from love to hate, and the greatness of her passion became the measure of her wrath, for very evilly she spoke of Graelent to the King. So long as the war endured,

Graelent remained in that realm. He spent all that he had upon his company, for the King grudged wages to his men. The Queen persuaded the King to this, counselling him that by withholding the pay of the sergeants, Graelent might in no wise flee the country, nor take service with another lord. So at the end Graelent was wonderfully downcast, nor was it strange that he was sad, for there remained nothing which he might pledge, but one poor steed, and when this was gone, no horse had he to carry him from the realm.

It was now the month of May, when the hours are long and warm. The burgess with whom Graelent lodged had risen early in the morning, and with his wife had gone to eat with neighbours in the town. No one was in the house except Graelent, no squire, nor archer, nor servant, save only the daughter of his host, a very courteous maid. When the hour for dinner was come she prayed the knight that they might sit at board together. But he had no heart for mirth, and seeking out his squire, bade him bridle and saddle his horse, for he had no care to eat.

"I have no saddle," replied the squire.

"Friend," said the demoiselle, "I will lend you bridle and saddle as well."

So when the harness was done upon him, Graelent mounted his horse, and went his way through the town, clad in a cloak of sorry fur, which he had worn overlong already. The townsfolk in the street turned and stared upon him, making a jest of his poverty, but of their jibes he took no heed, for such act but after their kind, and seldom show kindliness or courtesy.

Now without the town there spread a great forest, thick with trees, and through the forest ran a river.

Towards this forest Graelent rode, deep in heavy thought, and very dolent. Having ridden for a little space beneath the trees, he spied within a leafy thicket a fair white hart, whiter even than snow on winter branches. The hart fled before him, and Graelent followed so closely in her track that man and deer presently came together to a grassy lawn, in the midst of which sprang a fountain of clear, sweet water. Now in this fountain a demoiselle disported herself for her delight. Her raiment was set on a bush near by, and her two maidens stood on the bank, busied in their lady's service. Graelent forgot the chase at so sweet a sight, since never in his life had he seen so lovely a dame. For the lady was slender in shape and white, very gracious and dainty of colour, with laughing eyes and an open brow—certainly the most beautiful thing in all the world. Graelent dared not draw nigh the fountain for fear of troubling the dame, so he came softly to the bush to set hands upon her raiment. The two maidens marked his approach, and at their fright the lady turned, and calling him by name, cried with great anger—

"Graelent, put my raiment down, for it will profit you little even if you carry it away, and leave me naked in this wood. But if you are indeed too greedy of gain to remember your knighthood, at least return me my shift, and content yourself with my mantle, since it will bring you money, as it is very good."

"I am not a merchant's son," answered Graelent merrily, "nor am I a huckster to sell mantles in a booth. If your cloak were worth the spoil of three castles I would not now carry it from the bush. Come forth from your bathing, fair friend, and clothe your-

self in your vesture, for you have to say a certain word
to me."

"I will not trust myself to your hand, for you might
seize upon me," answered the lady; "and I tell you
frankly that I put no faith in your word, nor have
had any dealings with your school."

Then Graelent answered still more merrily—

"Lady, needs must I suffer your wrath. But at least
I will guard your raiment till you come forth from
the fountain; and, fairest, very dainty is your body in
my eyes."

When the lady knew that Graelent would not depart, nor render again her raiment, then she demanded surety that he would do her no hurt. This thing
was accorded between them, so she came forth from
the fountain, and did her vesture upon her. Then
Graelent took her gently by the left hand, and prayed
and required of her that she would grant him love
for love. But the lady answered—

"I marvel greatly that you should dare to speak to
me in this fashion, for I have little reason to think you
discreet. You are bold, sir knight, and overbold, to
seek to ally yourself with a woman of my lineage."

Sir Graelent was not abashed by the dame's proud
spirit, but wooed and prayed her gently and sweetly,
promising that if she granted him her love he would
serve her in all loyalty, and never depart therefrom all
the days of his life. The demoiselle hearkened to the
words of Graelent, and saw plainly that he was a
valiant knight, courteous and wise. She thought within
herself that should she send him from her, never
might she find again so sure a friend. Since then she

knew him worthy of her love, she kissed him softly, and spoke to him in this manner—

"Graelent, I will love you none the less truly, though we have not met until this day. But one thing is needful that our love may endure. Never must you speak a word by which this hidden thing may become known. I will furnish you with deniers in your purse, with cloth of silk, with silver and with gold. Night and day will I stay with you, and great shall be the love between us twain. You shall see me riding at your side, you may talk and laugh with me at your pleasure, but I must never be seen of your comrades, nor must they know aught concerning your bride. Graelent, you are loyal, brave and courteous, and comely enough to the view. For you I spread my snare at the fountain; for you shall I suffer heavy pains, as well I knew before I set forth on this adventure. Now must I trust to your discretion, for if you speak vainly and boastfully of this thing, then am I undone. Remain now for a year in this country, which shall be for you a home that your lady loves well. But noon is past, and it is time for you to go. Farewell, and a messenger shortly shall tell you that which I would have you do."

Graelent took leave of the lady, and she sweetly clasped and kissed him farewell. He returned to his lodging, dismounted from his steed, and entering within a chamber, leaned from the casement, considering this strange adventure. Looking towards the forest, he saw a varlet issue therefrom riding upon a palfrey. He drew rein before Graelent's door, and taking his feet from the stirrup, saluted the knight. So Graelent inquired from whence he rode, and of his name and business.

"Sir," answered he, "I am the messenger of your lady. She sends you this destrier by my hand, and would have me enter your service, to pay your servitors their wages and to take charge of your lodging."

When Graelent heard this message he thought it both good and fair. He kissed the varlet upon the cheek, and accepting his gift, caused the destrier—which was the noblest, the swiftest and the most speedy under the sun—to be led to the stable. Then the varlet carried his baggage to his master's chamber, and took therefrom a large cushion and a rich coverlet which he spread upon the couch. After this he drew thereout a purse containing much gold and silver, and stout cloth fitting for the knight's apparel. Then he sent for the host, and paying him what was owing, called upon him to witness that he was recompensed most largely for the lodging. He bade him also to seek out such knights as should pass through the town to refresh and solace themselves in the company of his lord. The host was a worthy man. He made ready a plenteous dinner, and inquired through the town for such poor knights as were in misease by reason of prison or of war. These he brought to the hostelry of Sir Graelent, and comforted them with instruments of music, and with all manner of mirth. Amongst them sat Graelent at meat, gay and debonair, and richly apparelled. Moreover, to these poor knights and the harpers Graelent gave goodly gifts, so that there was not a citizen in all the town who did not hold him in great worship, and regard him as his lord.

From this moment Graelent lived greatly at his ease, for not a cloud was in his sky. His lady came at will and pleasure; all day long they laughed and played together, and at night she lay softly at his side. What truer happiness might he know than this? Often, besides, he rode to such tournaments of the land as he was able, and all men esteemed him for a stout and worthy knight. Very pleasant were his days and his love, and if such things might last for ever he had nothing else to ask of life.

When a full year had passed by, the season drew to the feast of Pentecost. Now it was the custom of the King to summon at that tide his barons and all who held their fiefs of him to his Court for a rich banquet. Amongst these lords was bidden Sir Graelent. After men had eaten and drunk the whole day, and all were merry, the King commanded the Queen to put off her royal robes, and to stand forth upon the daïs. Then he boasted before the company—

"Lord barons, how seems it to you? Beneath the sky is there a lovelier queen than mine, be she maid, dame or demoiselle?"

So all the lords made haste to praise the Queen, and to cry and affirm that in all the world was neither maid nor wife so dainty, fresh and fair. Not a single voice but bragged of her beauty, save only that of Graelent. He smiled at their folly, for his heart remembered his friend, and he held in pity all those who so greatly rejoiced in the Queen. So he sat with covered head, and with face bent smiling to the board. The Queen marked his discourtesy, and drew thereto the notice of the King.

"Sire, do you observe this dishonour? Not one of these mighty lords but has praised the beauty of your wife, save Graelent only, who makes a mock of her. Always has he held me in envy and despite."

The King commanded Graelent to his throne, and
in the hearing of all bade the knight to tell, on his
faith as vassal to his liege, for what reason he had hid
his face and laughed.

"Sire," answered Graelent to the King, "sire, heark-
en to my words. In all the world no man of your lineage does so shameful a deed as this. You make your
wife a show upon a stage. You force your lords to
praise her just with lies, saying that the sun does not
shine upon her peer. One man will tell the truth to
your face, and say that very easily can be found a
fairer dame than she."

Right heavy was the King when he heard these
words. He conjured Graelent to tell him straightly if
he knew a daintier dame.

"Yes, sire, and thirty times more gracious than the
Queen."

The Queen was marvellously wrathful to hear this
thing, and prayed her husband of his grace to compel
the knight to bring that woman to the Court of whose
beauty he made so proud a boast.

"Set us side by side, and let the choice be made
between us. Should she prove the fairer, let him go in
peace; but if not, let justice be done on him for his
calumny and malice."

So the King bade his guards to lay hands on Graelent, swearing that between them never should be love
nor peace, nor should the knight issue forth from
prison, until he had brought before him her whose
beauty he had praised so much.

Graelent was held a captive. He repented him of
his hasty words, and begged the King to grant him
respite. He feared to have lost his friend, and sweated

grievously with rage and mortification. But though many of the King's house pitied him in his evil case, the long days brought him no relief, until a full year went by, and once again the King made a great banquet to his barons and his lieges. Then was Graelent brought to hall, and put to liberty, on such terms that he would return bringing with him her whose loveliness he had praised before the King. Should she prove so desirable and dear as his boast, then all would be well, for he had nought to fear. But if he returned without his lady, then he must go to judgment, and his only hope would be in the mercy of the King.

Graelent mounted his good horse and parted from the Court, sad and wrathful. He sought his lodging, and inquired for his servant, but might not find him. He called upon his friend, but the lady did not heed his voice. Then Graelent gave way to despair, and preferred death to life. He shut himself within his chamber, crying upon his dear one for grace and mercy, but from her he got neither speech nor comfort. So, seeing that his love had withdrawn herself from him by reason of his grievous fault, he took no rest by night or day, and held his life in utter despite. For a full year he lived in this piteous case, so that it was marvellous to those about him that he might endure his life.

On the day appointed, the sureties brought Graelent where the King was set in hall with his lords. Then the King inquired of Graelent where was now his friend.

"Sire," answered the knight, "she is not here, for in no wise might I find her. Now do with me according to your will."

'Sir Graelent," said the King, "very foully have you spoken. You have slandered the Queen, and given all my lords the lie. When you go from my hands never will you do more mischief with your tongue."

Then the King spoke with a high voice to his barons.

"Lords, I pray and command you to give judgment in this matter. You heard the blame that Graelent set upon me before all my Court. You know the deep dishonour that he fastened on the Queen. How may such a disloyal vassal deal honestly with his lord, for as the proverb tells, 'Hope not for friendship from the man who beats your dog!' "

The lords of the King's household went out from before him, and gathered themselves together to consider their judgment. They kept silence for a great space, for it was grievous to them to deal harshly with so valiant a knight. Whilst they thus refrained from words a certain page hastened unto them, and prayed them not to press the matter, for (said he) "even now two young maidens, the freshest maids in all the realm, seek the Court. Perchance they bring succour to the good knight, and, so it be the will of God, may deliver him from peril." So the lords waited right gladly, and presently they saw two damsels come riding to the palace. Very young were these maidens, very slender and gracious, and daintily cloaked in two fair mantles. So when the pages had hastened to hold their stirrup and bridle, the maidens dismounted from their palfreys, and entering within the hall came straight before the King.

"Sire," said one of the two damsels, "hearken now to me. My lady commands us to pray you to put back this cause for a while, nor to deliver judgment therein, since she comes to plead with you for the deliverance of this knight."

When the Queen heard this message she was filled with shame, and made speed to get her from the hall. Hardly had she gone than there entered two other damsels, whiter and more sweetly flushed even than their fellows. These bade the King to wait for a little, since their mistress was now at hand. So all men stared upon them, and praised their great beauty, saying that if the maids were so fair, what then must be the loveliness of the dame. When, therefore, the demoiselle came in her turn, the King's household stood upon their feet to give her greeting. Never did woman show so queenly to men's sight as did this lady riding to the hall. Passing sweet she was to see, passing simple and gracious of manner, with softer eyes and a daintier face than girl of mother born. The whole Court marvelled at her beauty, for no spot or blemish might be found in her body. She was richly dressed in a kirtle of vermeil silk, broidered with gold, and her mantle was worth the spoil of a king's castle. Her palfrey was of good race, and speedy; the harness and trappings upon him were worth a thousand livres in minted coin. All men pressed about her, praising her face and person, her simplicity and queenlihead. She came at a slow pace before the King, and dismounting from the palfrey, spoke very courteously in this fashion—

"Sire," said she, "hearken to me, and you, lord barons, give heed to my pleading. You know the words Graelent spake to the King, in the ears of men, when the Queen made herself a show before the lords, saying that often had he seen a fairer lady. Very hasty and foolish was his tongue, since he provoked the King to anger. But at least he told the truth when he said that there is no dame so comely but that very easily may be found one more sweet than she. Look now boldly upon my face, and judge you rightly in this quarrel between the Queen and me. So shall Sir Graelent be acquitted of this blame."

Then gazing upon her, all the King's household, lord and lackey, prince and page, cried with one voice that her favour was greater than that of the Queen. The King himself gave judgment with his barons that this thing was so; therefore was Sir Graelent acquitted of his blame, and declared a free man.

When judgment was given the lady took her leave of the King, and attended by her four damsels departed straightway from the hall upon her palfrey. Sir Graelent caused his white horse to be saddled, and mounting, followed hotly after her through the town. Day after day he rode in her track, pleading for pity and pardon, but she gave him neither good words nor bad in answer. So far they fared that at last they came to the forest, and taking their way through a deep wood rode to the bank of a fair, clear stream. The lady set her palfrey to the river, but when she saw that Graelent also would enter therein she cried to him—

"Stay, Graelent, the stream is deep, and it is death for you to follow."

Graelent took no heed to her words, but forced his horse to enter the river, so that speedily the waters closed above his head. Then the lady seized his bridle, and with extreme toil brought horse and rider back again to land.

"Graelent," said she, "you may not pass this river,

however mightily you pain yourself, therefore must you remain alone on this shore."

Again the lady set her palfrey to the river, but Graelent could not suffer to see her go upon her way without him. Again he forced his horse to enter the water; but the current was very swift and the stream was very deep, so that presently Graelent was torn from his saddle, and being borne away by the stream came very nigh to drown. When the four maidens saw his piteous plight they cried aloud to their lady, and said—

"Lady, for the love of God, take pity on your poor friend. See how he drowns in this evil case. Alas, cursed be the day you spake soft words in his ear, and gave him the grace of your love. Lady, look how the current hurries him to his death. How may your heart suffer him to drown whom you have held so close! Aid him, nor have the sin on your soul that you endured to let the man who loved you die without your help."

When the lady heard the complaint of her maidens, no longer could she hide the pity she felt in her heart. In all haste she turned her palfrey to the river, and entering the stream clutched her lover by the belt. Thus they won together to the bank. There she stripped the drowned man of his raiment, and wrapping him fast in her own dry mantle cherished him so meetly that presently he came again to life. So she brought him safely into her own land, and none has met Sir Graelent since that day.

But the Breton folk still hold firmly that Graelent yet liveth with his friend. His destrier, when he escaped him from the perilous river, grieved greatly for his master's loss. He sought again the mighty forest, yet never was at rest by night or day. No peace might he find, but ever pawed he with his hoofs upon the ground, and neighed so loudly that the noise went through all the country round about. Many a man coveted so noble a steed, and sought to put bit and bridle in his mouth, yet never might one set hands upon him, for he would not suffer another master. So each year in its season, the forest was filled with the cry and the trouble of this noble horse which might not find its lord.

This adventure of the good steed and of the stout knight, who went to the land of Faery with his love, was noised abroad throughout all Brittany, and the Bretons made a lay thereof which was sung in the ears of many people, and was called a Lay of the Death of Sir Graelent.

THE THREE THIEVES

THIS story tells that once upon a time there were three thieves faring together, who had robbed many people, both church folk and lay. One of these thieves was named Travers, but though he was in the company of two robbers, yet he was not altogether such as they. They, indeed, were thieves by descent as well as by choice, for their father was hanged for his misdeeds. The one was called Haimet, and the other Barat, but which was the more cunning workman at his trade it would be hard to tell.

The three companions were passing one day through a high and leafy wood, when Haimet spied a magpie's nest hidden within an oak. He went beneath the tree, and his sharp eyes quickly perceived that the bird was sitting upon her eggs. This thing he showed to Travers, and afterwards to his brother.

"Friends," said he, "would not he be a good thief who might take these eggs, and so softly descend the tree that the magpie knew nought thereof?"

"There is no man in the world who can do such a feat," answered Barat.

"Certes, there is such a man," said Haimet, "and you shall see him at his task, if you will only look at me."

Haimet set hands upon the oak, and climbed lightly up the great tree, as one who had no fear to fall. He came to the nest, and parting the straw softly from beneath, drew forth the eggs coyly and delicately. Then he descended to the ground with a merry heart, and addressing himself to his comrades, showed the eggs that he had stolen.

"Friends," said he, "here are the eggs, ready for boiling upon a fire!"

"Truly," said Barat, "no man's fingers are nimbler than yours, and if you can only return the eggs to the nest, why I will own freely that you are the most cunning thief of us all."

"Certes," answered Haimet, "they shall be set again beneath the bird, and not a shell of them all shall be broken."

So he came again to the oak, and mounted swiftly into the tree, hand over hand. Now he had gone but a little way when Barat hastened to the tree, and climbed therein even more lightly and surely than his brother. He followed him secretly from branch to branch, for Haimet was intent upon his task, and gave no thought to those he had left below. Then, whilst Haimet returned the eggs to the rifled nest, he stole the very breeches from his legs, and forthwith descended to the ground. When Travers saw this he was sick at heart, because he knew well he might never do such feats as these. Presently Haimet came down to his companions, and said—

"Friends, how seems it to you? Fingers like mine should pick up a good living."

"I know not how it looks to me," answered Barat. "Your fingers are quick enough, but your brains must be very dull, since they cannot procure you even hosen for your legs."

"Yes, truly, I have hosen, and those altogether new,

for it was but the other day I laid hands upon the cloth, and they reach to my very ankles."

"Are they so long as that?" said Barat; "shew them to us, and hide them not away."

Then Haimet lifted his tunic and stared upon his legs, for he was without breeches.

"Lord!" said he, "how can this have chanced? Where, then, are my hosen?"

"I do not think that you have any, fair fellow," said Travers. "There is no such thief as Barat, from here to Nevers, or so it seems to me. Cunning indeed is the thief who can steal from a thief. But for my part I am not meant for your trade, for I cannot spell even its A B C. A hundred times should I be taken in my simplicity, where you would escape by guile. I will return to my own village where I was married to my wife. Mad must I have been to forsake it to become a thief. I am neither fool nor idler, and know well how to toil in the fields, to winnow and to reap. With the help of God I am yet strong enough to gain my bread, so I go my way, and commend you to God His keeping."

So Travers parted from the company of the two thieves, and travelled by hill and dale till he came at last to his own country. His comely wife, Dame Maria, bore him no grudge for his absence, but welcomed his return with much joy, as was her husband's due. He settled down amongst his friends and acquaintance, and earned his living honestly and well. He prospered greatly, so that he had enough and to spare, both of this and of that. Now, towards Christmas, Travers killed a pig which he had fattened all the year. He hung the bacon from a rafter of his house, but better had he done, and much trouble would he have escaped, had he sold it in the village, as you will see who read this story.

On a day when Travers was cutting fagots within a coppice, Haimet and Barat, seeking what they might find, lighted on his house, and found Dame Maria spinning at her wheel. Then said these rogues whose business it was to cozen the simple—

"Dame, where is your husband?"

"Gentles," answered she, unknowing of these cheats, "he is in the wood, gathering fagots for the fire."

"May God prosper his work," said they devoutly.

So they seated themselves, and looked about the house, high and low, at larder and hearth-stone, in every nook and corner. Presently Barat, raising his head, saw the side of bacon hanging from the rafters. He drew the attention of Haimet to the meat, saying—

"Travers pains himself greatly to hide this bacon in his room. He fears lest we should live a little at his cost, or taste his savoury meat. Yet taste we will, if so we may."

Then they took their leave, and going a short distance, hid themselves behind a hedge, where each set to work upon the sharpening of a stake.

When Travers returned to his home—

"Husband," said his wife, Dame Maria, "two men have sought you who frightened me greatly, for I was alone in the house, and they would not tell me their business. They were mean and shifty to look upon, and there is not a thing in all the room that they have not taken stock of—not the bacon, nor anything else—knife, reaping-hook, nor axe, for their eyes were in every place at once."

"Well I know who they are and what they want of me," said Travers, "for they have seen me often. We have lost our bacon, I promise you, since Barat and Haimet have come to seek it for themselves. It is to no purpose that we have cured it in the smoke, of that I am very sure. In an evil hour I killed my pig, and certainly it were better to have sold it last Saturday when I was able."

"Husband," answered the wife, "if you take the bacon down from the ceiling, perchance these thieves may not find it when they come."

Therefore, because of the importunity of his wife, Travers mounted on a stool and cut the cord, so that the bacon fell upon the floor. But not knowing where to bestow the meat, they let it remain even where it had fallen, having first covered it with the vessel in which they kneaded their bread. Then, sad at heart, they went to bed to take what rest they might.

When the night was come, those who were so desirous of the bacon came to the house, and with their stakes made a hole in the wall near to the threshold, a hole so large that you might have trundled a millstone therein. Thereby they entered softly, and groped warily about the house. Now Barat went from stool to table till he came beneath the rafter from whence the bacon hung. He knew by touch that the cord was severed, and he whispered in his brother's ear that he had not found the meat, "But," said the thief, "Travers is a fool if he thinks to conceal it for long."

Then they listened in the darkness of the room to the breathing of those upon the bed.

Travers did not dare to sleep, and finding that his wife was becoming drowsy, roused her, saying—

"Wife, this is no time for sleep. I shall go about the house to see that all is fast."

"Do not leave me," answered his wife.

But Travers, who was a prudent man, rose from his bed to make sure of all his goods. He came to the kneading trough, and raising it a little from the ground, felt the bacon safely beneath. Then taking a great axe in his hand he went out to visit his cow in her byre.

Barat came swiftly to the bed, like the bold and cunning thief he was.

"Marion," said he, "fair sister, I have a certain thing to ask you, but dare not do so, for fear you think me mad."

"That I will never deem you, husband, by St. Paul; but I will counsel you to the best of my power."

"I slept so soundly that I cannot remember where we bestowed the bacon yester night, so bemused am I with dreams."

"God help you, husband, to find more seasonable jests; is it not hid beneath the bin upon the floor?"

"In God's name, sister, you speak truly, and I will go to feel if it is yet there."

Being desirous to keep his word, Barat lifted the trough and drew forth the bacon. Then he rejoined Haimet, who was near by, and the two thieves hastened towards the coppice, making much of each other because of the success of their trick.

Now Travers returned to his bed, first carefully fastening his doors.

"Certes," said his wife, "dazed you must have been to ask me what had become of our bacon."

"God help me," cried Travers, "when did I ask you this question?"

"Why, but now, husband."

"Sister, our bacon has walked off. Never shall we see it more, unless I may steal it from these thieves. But they are the most cunning robbers in all the land."

Travers went out forthwith in quest of the rogues who had carried off his bacon. He took a short cut through a field of wheat, and following the path very swiftly, presently found himself between the tricksters and the wood. Haimet was very near to cover, but Barat went more heavily, seeing that his load was right heavy. So Travers, being anxious to take his own again, quickened his steps, and coming to him said—

"Give it to me, for you are weary, seeing you have carried it so long a road. Sit down now, and take a little rest."

Barat, thinking that he had met with Haimet, gladly placed the bacon on the shoulders of Travers, and went his way. But Travers turned him back to his own house, and hastened towards his home by the nearest path. Now Barat, deeming that Haimet followed after, ran towards the wood until he overtook his brother. When he knew him again he had great fear, because he thought him behind. But when Haimet saw him stagger, he cried out, "Let me bear the bacon for a while. I think it little likely that I shall fall beneath its weight, as you are near to do. Certainly you are overdone."

"God give me health," answered Barat, "for Travers has made a fool of us. It is he who carries his bacon on his own shoulders. But the game is not finished yet, and I have yet a throw to make."

Travers proceeded on his way in quietness and peace, as one who had nought to fear from any man. But Barat, wet with haste, overtook him in the end. He had taken off his shirt and wrapped it about his head like a coif, and as much as he was able bore himself in the semblance of a woman.

"Alas," cried he, "very nearly am I dead by reason of the loss and mischief dealt me by these wicked men. God, what has become of my husband, who has suffered so many things at their hands?"

Thinking that his wife was speaking to him, Travers held forth the bacon.

"Sister," said he, "God is yet above the Devil. You see we have again our own."

Then he, who never thought to lay hands upon the meat, seized upon it greedily.

"Do not wait for me, husband, but get to bed as quickly as you can, for now you may sleep without any fear."

So Travers returned to his own house, and Barat hastened to his brother, bearing the bacon with him.

When Travers found his wife in tears—

"Certes, Mary," said he, "all this has come upon us by reason of our sins. I thought to charge your shoulders with our bacon in the garden, but now I know well that these rogues have bestowed it upon theirs. Heavens, I wonder where he learned to play the part of a woman so bravely in manner and in speech! Hard is the lesson I am set to learn in school, because of a flitch of bacon. But, please God, I will find them this night, yea, though I walk till I have no sole to my shoe, and supplant them yet."

Travers took the path leading to the wood, and entering in the coppice, saw the red blaze of a fire which these two thieves had litten. He heard their voices lifted in dispute, so he concealed himself behind an oak, and listened to their words. At the end Barat and Haimet agreed that it were better to eat the bacon forthwith, lest a new cast of the dice should go against them. Whilst they went to seek dry cones and brushwood for the fire, Travers crept privily to the oak beneath which it was burning. But the wood was damp and green, so that more smoke and smother came from that fire than flame. Then Travers climbed into the tree, and by the aid of bough and branch came at last to the place where he would be. The two thieves returned presently with cones and brambles. These they threw upon the fire in handfuls, saying that very soon it would grill their bacon, and Travers hearkened to their speech. He had stripped himself to his shirt, and hung from a limb of the oak by his arm. Now, in a while, Haimet lifted his eyes to the tree, and saw above him the hanged man, tall, grotesque and horrible to see, naked in his very shirt.

"Barat," whispered he, "our father is spying upon us. Behold him hanging from this branch in a very hideous fashion. Surely it is he come back to us, is it not?"

"God help me," cried Barat, "it seems to me that he is about to fall."

Then because of their fear the two thieves fled from that place, without leisure to eat, or to bear away, the bacon they had stolen.

When Travers marked their flight he tarried no

longer in the oak, but taking his bacon, returned straightway to his house, with none to give him nay. His wife praised him to his face, saying—

"Husband, you are welcome home, for you have proven your worth. Never did there live a braver man than you."

"Sister," said he, "take wood from the cellar, and make a fire. Certainly we must eat our bacon, if we would call it our own."

Dame Maria lighted a fire with fagots upon the hearth; she put water in the cauldron, and hung it on the hook above the fire. Travers for his part carefully cut the bacon for which he had suffered so great trouble, and put it in the pot till all was full. When this was done—

"Fair sister," said he, "watch by the fire, if you can keep awake. I have not slept this night, and will rest a little on the bed. But I will not take off my clothes, because I still am troubled of these thieves."

"Husband," answered she, "ill luck go with them. Sleep soundly and in peace, for there is none to do you wrong."

So Dame Maria kept vigil whilst Travers slept, for very greatly had he need of rest.

During this time Barat lamented in the wood, for well he knew, when he found the bacon gone, that Travers had played this trick upon them.

"Certes," said he, "we have lost the meat because of our fearful hearts, and it belongs to Travers by right of courage. A good breakfast he will make, for he deems that none can take it from him. He will look upon us as dirt, if we leave it in his hands. Let us go to his house and mark where he has bestowed it."

The two thieves hastened to the door of Travers' house. Barat set his eye to a crevice therein, and saw a sight which gave him little joy, for the pot was boiling upon the fire.

"Haimet," said he, "the bacon is cooking, and much I grieve that there is none for us."

"Let it boil in peace till it is fit for eating," answered Haimet. "I shall not give Travers quittance in this matter till he has paid me wages for my toil."

Haimet sought a long stake which he cut from a hazel tree, and sharpened it with his knife. Then he climbed upon the roof of the house, and uncovered a little space above the spot where the cauldron boiled upon the fire. Through this opening he could see the wife of Travers sound asleep, for she was weary of her vigil, and nodded over the hearth. Haimet lowered the rod, which he had sharpened like a dart, and struck it in the pot so adroitly that he drew forth a portion of the bacon from out the cauldron. This he raised cunningly to the roof, and had great joy of his fishing. Then awoke Travers from his sleep, and saw this thing, and marked the thief, who was both malicious and strong.

"Gossip, upon my roof," said he, "it is not reasonable of you to strip the covering from over my head. In this manner we shall never come to an end. Climb down; let us give and take. Let each of us have his share of the bacon."

So Haimet descended from the roof, and the bacon was taken from the cauldron. Dame Maria divided the meat into three portions, for the thieves had no care to let Travers part the lots. The two brothers took two portions, and Travers one; but his was not the best, for all that he had nourished the pig.

For this reason was the proverb made, oh, gentles, that "Bad is the company of thieves."

THE FRIENDSHIP OF AMIS AND AMILE

IN the days of Pepin, King of the Franks, a boy was
born in the Castle of Bericain to a father of Allemaigne, of noble descent and of great holiness. His
father and mother, who had no other child, vowed to
God and to St. Peter and St. Paul that if God vouchsafed him breath he should be carried to Rome for his
baptism. At the same hour a vision was seen of the
Count of Alverne—whose wife was near her day—in
which he saw the Apostle of Rome, who baptized
many children in his palace, and confirmed them with
the anointing of holy oil. When the Count awoke from
his sleep he inquired of the wise men of those parts
what this thing might mean. Then a certain wise old
man, having heard his words, by the counsel of God
made answer, and said—

"Rejoice greatly, Count, for a son shall now be born
to thee great in courage and in virtue, and thou shalt
carry him to Rome, so that he may be baptized by the
Apostle."

So the Count rejoiced in his heart, and he and his
people praised the counsel of that ancient man.

The child was born, and cherished dearly, and when
he was of the age of two years his father prepared to
carry him to Rome, according to his purpose. On his
way he came to the city of Lucca, and there fell in
with a certain nobleman of Allemaigne who was on
pilgrimage to Rome, that there he might baptize his
son. Each greeted the other, and inquired of his name
and business; and when they knew they were in the
like case, and bound on the same errand, they took

each other as companion with a kind heart, and voyaged together to Rome. The two children, also, loved so dearly, that one would not eat save the other ate with him; so that they fed from the same dish, and lay in the one bed. In such manner as this the fathers carried the boys before the Apostle at Rome, and said to him—

"Holy Father, whom we believe and know to be seated in the chair of St. Peter the Apostle, we, the Count of Alverne, and the Chatelain of Castle Bericain, humbly pray your Holiness that you would deign to baptize the sons they have carried here from a distant land, and to accept this humble offering from their hands."

Then the Pope made answer—

"It is very meet to come with such a gift before me, but of such I have no need. Give it, therefore, to the poor, who cry for alms. Right willingly will I baptize the children, and may the Father, the Son and the Holy Ghost ever fold them close in the love of the Holy Trinity."

So at that one time the Apostle baptized the two children in St. Saviour's Church, and he gave to the son of the Count of Alverne the name of Amile, and to the son of the Chatelain of Castle Bericain gave he the name of Amis. Many a knight of Rome held them at the font, and answered in their name as god-parents, according to the will of God. Then, when the Sacrament of Baptism was at an end, the Apostle commanded to be brought two wooden cups, fair with gold and set with costly stones, of one workmanship, size and fashion, and these he handed to the children, saying—

"Take this gift in witness that I have baptized you in St. Saviour's Church."

So the knights received the cups with great joy, and rendered him grace for his gift, and parting from thence repaired each to his own home in all comfort and solace.

To the child of the Knight of Bericain God also gave a gift, the gift of such wise understanding that men might almost believe that he was another Solomon.

When Amis was of the age of thirty years a fever seized upon his father, and he began to admonish his son in words such as these—

"Fair, dear son, my end is near at hand, but thou shalt tarry for a season, and be thine own lord. Firstly, fair son, observe the commandments of God, and be of the chivalry of Jesus Christ. Keep faith with thy overlords, and turn not thy back on thy companions and thy friends. Defend the widow and the orphan; be pitiful to the captive and to all in need; think every day upon that day which shall be thy last. Forsake not the society and friendship of the son of the Count of Alverne, for the Apostle of Rome baptized you together on one day, and graced you with one gift. Are you not alike in all things—in beauty, in comeliness, and in strength, so that whosoever sees you, thinks you to be sons of one mother?"

Having spoken these words, he was houselled of the priest, and died in our Lord; and his son gave him fitting burial, and paid him all such service as is meetly required for the dead.

After the death of his father divers evil persons wrought Amis much mischief, because of the envy they felt towards him; but nevertheless he bore them no ill will, and patiently suffered all the wrong and malice that they did. Let me tell you, then, without more words, that such was his case that he and his servants were cast forth from the heritage of his fathers, and driven from the gate of his own keep. But when he had called to mind the words of his father, he said to those who journeyed with him in the way—

"The wicked have spoiled me wrongfully of my inheritance, yet have I good hope that the Lord is on my side. Come now, let us seek the Court of Count Amile, my comrade and my friend. Peradventure he will give us of his goods and lands; but if not, then will we gather to Hildegarde, the Queen, wife of King Charles of France, the stay and support of the disinherited."

So those of his company made answer that they would follow where he led, and would serve him as his men. They rode, therefore, to the court of the Count, but might not find him, for reason that he had passed to Bericain to comfort Amis, his companion, because of the death of his father. When Amile might not find Amis, he departed from the castle, greatly vexed, and resolved within himself that he would not solace himself in his own fief until he had met with Amis, his friend. Therefore he rode on this quest through France and Allemaigne, seeking news of him from all his kindred, but finding none.

Now Amis, together with his company, for his part sought diligently for Amile his friend, until it chanced that on a day a certain lord gave him harbourage, and at his bidding Amis told him of this adventure. Then said the nobleman—

"Dwell ye with me, sir knights, and I will give my daughter to your lord, because of the wisdom men report of him, and you, for your own part, shall be made rich in silver, in gold and in lands."

They rejoiced greatly at his word, and the wedding feast was celebrated with marvellous joy. But when they had tarried in that place for one year and six months, Amis called together his ten companions and spake to them.

"We are recreant, inasmuch as we have forgotten all this while to seek for Amile."

So he left two men-at-arms, together with his precious cup, and set forth towards Paris.

Now for the space of nearly two years Amile had sought for Amis without pause or rest. Drawing near to Paris he lighted upon a pilgrim and asked of him if perchance he knew aught of Amis, whom evil men had hunted from his lands. The palmer said "Nay," wherefore Amile divested himself of his cloak, and gave it to the pilgrim, saying—

"Pray thou to our Lord and His saints for me that they give me grace to meet Amis, my friend."

So he saluted the pilgrim, and went his way to Paris, seeking in every place for news of Amis his friend, and finding none. But the pilgrim, passing swiftly upon his road, came upon Amis about the hour of vespers, and they saluted each the other. Then Amis inquired of the palmer whether he had seen or heard, in any land or realm, aught of Amile, the son of the Count of Alverne.

"What manner of man art thou," answered the palmer all astonied, "that thou makest mock of a pilgrim? Thou seemest to me that very Amile who but this morn sought of me if I had seen Amis, his friend. I know not for what reason thou hast changed thine apparel, thy company, thy horses and thy arms, nor why thou askest of me the same question thou didst require at nine hours of the morn when thou gavest me this cloak."

"Be not angry with me," said Amis, "for I am not the man you deem; but I am Amis who searches for his friend Amile."

So he gave him money from his pouch, and prayed him that he would require of our Lord that He might grant him grace to find Amile.

"Hasten quickly to Paris," said the pilgrim, "and there shalt thou find him whom so fondly thou seekest."

So Amis hastened instantly to the city.

It chanced upon the morrow that Amile departed from Paris, and took his ease within a daisied meadow near by the pleasant waters of the Seine. Whilst he ate there with his knights there came that way Amis with his men-at-arms. So Amile and his company armed themselves forthwith, and rode forth before them at adventure. Then Amis said to his companions—

"Behold these French knights who seek to do us a mischief. Stand stoutly together, and so shall we defend our lives. If we but escape this peril soon shall we be within the walls of Paris, and sweetly shall we be entreated at the palace of the King."

Then drew the two companies together with loosened rein, with lance in rest, and with brandished sword, in such fashion that it seemed as if none might escape alive from the fury of that onset. But God, the all powerful, Who knoweth all, and bringeth to a good end the travail of the just, suffered not that spears should meet in that encounter. So when they were near at hand Amis cried aloud—

"Who are you, knights, that are so eager to slay Amis the Banished and his companions?"

When Amile heard these words he knew well the voice of Amis, his comrade, so he answered him—

"Oh thou, Amis, most dear, sweet as rest to my labour, know me for Amile, son of the Count of Alverne, who have not given over my quest for thee these two whole years."

Then forthwith they lighted from their steeds, and clasped and kissed each the other, giving grace to God Who granteth the treasure to the seeker. Moreover, upon the guard of Amile's sword, wherein was set a holy relic, they swore faith, and friendship, and fellowship to death, the one with the other. So set they forth from that place, riding together to the Court of Charles, the King of France. There they moved amongst the lords, young, discreet and wise, fair to see, shapen wondrously alike in form and face, beloved of all men and held of all in honour. There, too, the King received them with much courtesy, making of Amis his treasurer, and to Amile gave he the office of seneschal.

In this fashion they tarried long with the King, but at the end of three years Amis said to Amile—

"Fair, sweet companion, I desire greatly to see my wife, whom I have left so long. Stay thou at Court, and for my part I will return so soon as I may. But have thou no dealings with the daughter of the King, and, more than all, beware and keep thee from the malice of Arderay the felon knight."

"I will observe thy bidding," answered Amile, "but make no long tarrying from my side."

On these words Amis departed from the Court; but Amile for his part saw with his eyes that the daughter of the King was fair, and knew the princess, in love, as soon as he was able. Thus the commandment and the warning of Amis, his companion, passed quickly from his mind; yet think not too hardly of the young man forasmuch that he was not more holy than David, nor wiser than Solomon, David's son.

Whilst Amile was busied with these matters there came to him Arderay, the traitor, full of envy, and said—

"Thou dost not know, comrade, thou dost not know that Amis has stolen gold from the King's treasury, and therefore hath he taken flight. Since things are thus I require that you swear to me fealty of friendship and of brotherhood, and I will swear to you the like oath on the holy Gospels."

Having pledged such troth as this, Amile feared not to betray his secret to the felon knight. Now when Amile bore bason and ewer to the King, that he might wash his hands, then said that false Arderay to his lord—

"Take no water from the hands of this recreant, Sir King, for he is worthier of death than of life, since he has plucked from the Queen's daughter the flower of her maidenhood."

When Amile heard this thing he was so fearful that he fell upon the floor, and answered not a word, so that the courteous King raised him to his feet, and said—

"Have no fear, Amile, but stand up and acquit thee of this blame."

Then Amile stood upon his feet and said—

"Sir King, give no ready credence to the lies of this traitor Arderay, for well I know that you are an upright judge, turning neither for love nor hate out of the narrow way. Grant me, therefore, time for counsel with my friends, so that I may purge myself of this charge before you, and in single combat with Arderay, the traitor, prove him to be a liar before all your Court."

The King gave to both champions till three hours after noon that each might take counsel with his friends, and bade that at such time they should stand before him to fulfil their devoir. At the appointed hour they came before the King. With Arderay for friend and witness came Herbert the Count; but Amile found none to stand at his side, save only Hildegarde, the Queen. So sweetly did the lady plead his cause that she prevailed upon her lord to grant Amile such further respite for counsel that he might seek Amis, his friend; yet nevertheless only on such covenant that if Amile returned not on the appointed day the lady should be banished ever from the royal bed.

Whilst Amile was on his way to take counsel with his friend, he chanced on Amis, his comrade, who repaired to the Court of the King. So he alighted from his steed, and kneeling at the feet of his companion, said—

"Oh thou, my one hope of surety, I have not obeyed the charge you laid upon me, and am truly blamed by reason of my dealings with the daughter of the

King. Therefore must I endure ordeal of battle with the false Arderay."

"Let us leave here our companions," returned Amis, sighing, "and enter in this wood to make the matter clear."

Then Amis, having heard, reproached Amile, and said—

"Let us now exchange our garments and our horses, and thou, for thy part, get thee gone to my house, whilst I ride to do judgment by combat for thee upon this traitor."

But Amile answered him—

"How then may I go about thine house, seeing that I know not thy wife nor thy household, nor ever have looked upon their face?"

And Amis replied—

"Very easily mayest thou do this thing, so thou dost but walk prudently; but take thou good heed to have no dealings with my wife."

Thereupon the two companions departed one from the other, with tears; Amis riding to the Court of the King in the guise of Amile, and Amile to the house of his comrade in the guise of Amis. Now the wife of Amis, seeing him draw near, hastened to embrace him whom she thought was her lord, and would have kissed him. But Amile said—

"Is this a time for play? I have matter for tears rather than for claspings, for since I parted from thee have I suffered many bitter griefs, yea, and yet must suffer."

And that night as they made ready to lie together in one bed, Amile set his naked sword between the twain, and said to his brother's wife—

"Beware lest thy body draw near in any wise to mine, for then will I slay thee with this sword."

In such fashion passed the night, and every night, until Amis repaired secretly to the castle to know certainly whether Amile kept faith and word in this matter of his wife.

The day appointed for the combat now was come, and the Queen awaited Amile, sick of heart; for Arderay, that traitor, cried aloud, that certainly ought she never to come near the King's bed, since she had suffered and consented to Amile's dealings with her maid. Whilst Arderay boasted thus, Amis entered within the Court of the King at the hour of noon, clad in the apparel of his comrade, and said—

"Right debonair and Lord Justicier of this realm, here stand I to seek ordeal of battle with this false Arderay, because of the blame he has laid upon me, the Queen, and the Princess, her child."

Then answered the King right courteously—

"Be stout of heart, oh Count, for if you prove Arderay to be false I will give thee my daughter Belisant to wife."

On the morning of the morrow Arderay and Amis rode into the lists, armed from plume to heel, in the presence of the King and of much people. But the Queen with a great company of maidens and widows and dames went from church to church, giving gifts of money and of torches, and praying God for the safety of the champion of her daughter. Now Amis considered in his heart that should he slay Arderay he would be guilty of his blood before the eyes of God, and if he were overthrown then would it be a shame to him for all his days. So he spake in such manner as this to Arderay.

"Foul counsel hast thou followed, Sir Count, so ardently to seek my death, and to thrust this life of thine into grievous peril of hurt. So thou wilt withdraw the reproach thou hast fastened upon me, and avoid this mortal strife, thou canst have of me friendship and loyal service."

But Arderay was right wroth at these words, and replied—

"No care have I for friendship or service of thine; rather will I swear to the truth as that truth is, and smite thy head from thy shoulders."

Then Arderay swore that his foe had done wrong to the daughter of the King, and Amis made oath that he lied. Thereupon, incontinent they drove together, and with mighty strokes strove one against the other from the hour of tierce till it was nones. And at nones Arderay fell within the lists; and Amis struck off his head.

The King lamented that Arderay was dead, but rejoiced that his daughter was proved clean from stain. He gave the Princess to Amis for dame, and with her, as dowry, a mighty sum in gold and silver, and a city near by the sea where they might dwell. So Amis rejoiced greatly in his bride; and returned as quickly as he might to the castle where he had hidden Amile, his companion. When Amile saw him hastening homewards with many horsemen, he was sore adread that Amis was overthrown, and made ready to escape. But Amis sent messages to him that he should return in all surety, since he had avenged him upon Arderay, and thus, by proxy, was he married to the daughter of the King. So Amile repaired from that place, and dwelt with his dame in that city which was her heritage.

Now Amis abode with his wife, but by the permission of God he became a leper, and his sickness was so heavy upon him that he could not leave his bed, for whom God loveth him He chasteneth. His wife—who was named Obias—for this cause hated him sorely, and sought his death many a time in shameful fashion. When Amis perceived her malice he called to him two of his men-at-arms, Azonem and Horatus, and said to them—

"Deliver me from the hands of this wicked woman, and take with you my cup secretly, and bear us to the tower of Bericain."

When they drew near to the castle men came out before them asking of the sickness and of the man whom they carried there. Then they answered that this was Amis, their lord, who was a leper, for which cause they prayed them to show him some pity. But mercilessly they beat the sergeants, and tumbled Amis forth from the litter in which he was borne, crying—

"Flee swiftly from hence, if ye care aught for your lives."

Then Amis wept grievously, and said—

"Oh Thou, God most pitiful and compassionate, grant me to die, or give me help in this my extremity."

Again he said to the men-at-arms—

"Carry me now to the church of the Father of Rome; perchance God of His loving kindness will there give alms to the beggar."

When they were come to Rome, Constantine the Apostle, full of pity and of sanctity, together with many a knight of those who had held Amis at the font, came before him and supplied the wants of Amis and his servants. But after three years a great famine came upon the city—a famine so grievous that the father put his very offspring from the door. Then Azonem and Horatus spake to Amis—

"Fair sir, bear witness how loyally we have served you from the death of your father, even to this day, and that never have we done against your bidding. But now we dare no longer to bide with you, since we have no heart to die of hunger. For this cause we pray you to acquit us of our service, so that we may avoid this mortal pestilence."

Then answered Amis in his tears—

"Oh, my dear children, not servants but sons, my only comfort, I pray you for the love of God that you forsake me not here, but that you bear me to the city of my comrade, Count Amile."

And these, willing to obey his commandment, carried him to that place where Amile lay. Now when they came before the court of Amile's house they began to sound their clappers, as the leper is wont to do; so when Amile heard the sound thereof he bade a servitor of his to carry to the sick man bread and meat, and the cup which was given to him at Rome brimed with rich wine. When the man-at-arms had done the bidding of his lord, he came to him again, and said—

"Sir, by the faith which is your due, if I held not your cup within my hand, I should believe it to be the cup that the sick man beareth even now, for they are alike in workmanship and height."

And Amile said to him—

"Go quickly, and bring him hither to me."

When the leper was come before his comrade, Amile inquired of him who he was, and how he came to own such a cup.

"I am of Castle Bericain," said he, "and the cup was given me by the Apostle of Rome who baptized me."

When Amile heard these words he knew within himself that this was Amis, his comrade, who had delivered him from death, and given him the daughter of the King of France as dame. So at once he fell upon his neck, and began to weep and lament his evil case, kissing and embracing him. When his wife heard this thing she ran forth with fallen hair, weeping and making great sorrow, for she bore in mind that this was he who had done judgment on Arderay. Forthwith they set him in a very fair bed, and said to him—

"Tarry with us, fair sir, until the will of God is done on you, for all that we have is as thine own."

So he dwelt with them, he and his two men-at-arms likewise.

Now on a night when Amis and Amile lay together in a chamber, without other company, God sent Raphael, His angel, to Amis, who spake him thus—

"Amis, sleepest thou?"

And he, deeming that Amile had called him, answered—

"I sleep not, fair dear companion."

And the angel said to him—

"Thou hast well spoken, for thou art the companion of the citizens of Heaven, and like Job and Tobit hast suffered all things meekly and with patience. I am Raphael, an angel of our Lord, who am come to show thee medicine for thy healing, for God hath heard thy prayers. Thou must bid **Amile**, thy comrade, to slay his two children with the sword, and wash thee in their blood, that thus thy body may become clean."

Then Amis replied—

"This be far from me, that my comrade be blood-guilty for my health."

But the angel said—

"It is meet that he should do this thing."

On these words the angel departed from him.

Now Amile also, in his sleep, had heard these words, and he awoke, and said—

"Comrade, who is this who hath spoken to thee?"

And Amis answered that no man had spoken.

"But I prayed our Lord, as is my wont."

But Amile said—

"It is not thus, but some one hath spoken with thee."

Then he rose from the bed, and went to the door of the chamber, and finding it fast, said—

"Tell me, fair brother, who hath said to thee these hidden words."

Then Amis began to weep bitterly, and denied not that it was Raphael, the angel of our Lord, who had said to him, "Amis, our Lord sends word to thee that thou biddest Amile to slay his two children with the sword, and to wash thee in their blood, that thou mayest be clean of thy leprosy."

And Amile was sorely distressed on hearing these words, and said—

"Amis, gladly have I given thee sergeant and damsel and all the riches that I had, and in fraud thou feignest that the angel hath bidden me to slay my two little ones with the sword."

Then Amis broke out into weeping, and said—

"I know that I have told thee of a grievous matter, but not of mine own free will; I pray thee therefore that thou cast me not forth from thy house."

And Amile answered him that the covenant he had made with him he would not depart from till the hour of death. "But I adjure thee by the faith between me and thee, and by our fellowship, and by the baptism given to us twain at Rome, that thou tell me truly whether it was man or angel who spoke to thee of this thing."

And Amis made reply—

"So truly as the angel hath held converse with me this night, so may God make me clean of my infirmity."

Then Amile began to weep privily, and to consider within his heart. "If this man was willing to die in my stead before the King, why then should I not slay mine own for him! He hath kept faith with me even unto death: shall I not therefore keep faith with him! Abraham was saved by faith, and by faith have the saints proved mightier than kings. Yea, God saith in the Gospel, 'Whatsoever ye would that men should do unto you, even so do unto them.'"

Then Amile delayed no more, but went to his wife's chamber, and bade her to attend the Divine Office; so the Countess sought the church, as was her wont to do, and the Count took his sword and went to the bed where lay the children, and they were asleep. And bending above them he wept bitterly, and said—

"Hath any man heard of such father who was willing to slay his child? Alas, alas, my children, no longer shall I be your father, but your cruel murderer."

The children awoke because of their father's tears which fell upon them, and looking upon his face began to laugh. Since therefore they were about the age of three years he said to them—

"Your laughter will turn to tears, for now your innocent blood shall be shed."

He spoke thus, and cut off their heads; and making straight their limbs upon the bed, he set their heads to their bodies, and covered all with the coverlet, as if they slept. So he washed his companion with the blood of that slaying, and said—

"Lord God, Jesus Christ, Who hast bidden men to keep faith on earth, and didst cleanse the leper with Thy word, deign Thou to make clean my comrade, for love of whom I have shed the blood of my children."

Straightway was Amis made whole of his leprosy, and they gave grace to our Lord with great joy, saying—

"Blessed be God, the Father of our Lord Jesus Christ, who saveth those who put their trust in Him."

And Amile clad his comrade from his own rich apparel and passing to the church to render thanks in that place, the bells rang without ringers, as was the will of God. When the people of the city heard thereof they hastened to behold this marvel. Now the wife of the Count, when she saw the twain walking together, began to question which was her husband, and said, "Well I know the vesture which they wear, but which is Amile, that I know not," and the Count said—

"I am Amile, and this, my companion, is Amis, who is healed."

Then the Countess marvelled greatly, and said—

"Easy is it to see that he is healed, but much desire I to know the manner of that healing."

"Render thanks to our Lord," returned the Count, "nor seek curiously of the fashion of that cleansing."

The hour of tierce was now come, and neither of the parents had yet entered in the chamber where the children lay, but the father went heavily for reason of their death. The Countess asked therefore for her sons that they might share in the joy, but the Count replied—

"Nay, dame, but let the children sleep."

Then entering by himself within the chamber to bewail his children, he found them playing in the bed; and about their necks, in the place of that mortal wound, showed as it were a crimson thread. So he clasped them in his arms, and bore them to their mother, saying—

"Dame, rejoice greatly, for thy sons whom I had slain with the sword, at the bidding of the angel, are alive, and by their blood is Amis cleansed and healed."

When the Countess heard this thing she said—

"Count, why was I not with thee to gather the blood of my children, that I too might have washed Amis, thy comrade and my lord?"

And the Count answered her—

"Dame, let be these words; rather let us dedicate ourselves to our Lord, who hath wrought such marvels in our house."

So from that day, even unto their deaths, they lived together in perfect chastity; and for the space of ten days the people of that city held high festival. But on that very day that Amis was made clean, the devil seized upon his wife, and breaking her neck, carried off her soul.

After these things Amis rode to the castle of Bericain, and laid siege thereto, and sat before it for so long a time that those within the castle yielded themselves into his hand. He received them graciously, forgetting his anger against them, and forgiving them the wrongs that they had done, so that from thenceforth he dwelt peaceably amongst them, and with him, in his own house, lived the elder son of Count Amile. There he served our Lord with all his heart.

Now Adrian, being at this time Pope of Rome, sent letters to Charles, King of France, praying him to come to his aid against Didier, King of the Lombards, who wrought much mischief to him and the Church. Now Charles lay in the town of Thionville, and to that place came Peter, the envoy of the Apostle, with messages from the Pope praying him to hasten to the succour of Holy Church. For this cause Charles sent letters to the said Didier requiring him to render to the Holy Father the cities and all other things which he had wrongfully seized, and promising that if he would do this thing the said Charles would send him in return the sum of forty thousand pieces of gold, in gold and silver. But he would not do right, neither for prayers nor for gifts.

Then the stout King Charles summoned to his aid all his men—bishops, abbots, dukes, princes, marquises, and other stout knights. Divers of these he sent to Cluses to guard the pass, and of this number was Albin, Bishop of Angers, a man of great holiness.

King Charles himself, with a large company of spears, drew towards Cluses by the way of Mont Cenis, and he sent Bernard, his uncle, with other knights, thither by way of Mont Saint-Bernard. The vanguard of the host said that Didier, with all his strength, lay at Cluses, which town he had made strong with iron chains and works of stone. Whilst Charles approached to Cluses he sent messengers to Didier, requiring him to render to the Holy Father the cities which he had taken, but he would not heed his prayer. Again Charles sent him other letters demanding three children of the Justices of Lombardy as hostages, until such time as he had yielded up the cities of the Church; in which case for his part he would return to France with all his spears, without battle and without malice. But neither for this nor for that would he stint.

When God the All-powerful had beheld the hard heart and the malice of this Didier, and found that the French desired greatly to return, He put so fearful a trembling in the hearts of the Lombards that they took to flight, though there was none that pursued, leaving behind them their tents and all their harness. So Charles and his host followed after them, and Frenchman, German, Englishman and divers other people entered hot after them into Lombardy.

Amis and Amile were of the host, and very near to the person of the King. Always they strove to follow our Lord in good works, and were constant in fast, in vigil, in giving of alms, in succouring the widow and the orphan, in assuaging often the wrath of the King, in patient suffering of evil men, and in piteous dealings within the Roman realm.

But though Charles had a great army drawn together in Lombardy, King Didier feared not to come before him with his little host—for there where Didier had a priest, Charles had a bishop; where one had a monk, the other had an abbot; if this had a knight, that had a prince; if Didier had a man-at-arms, then Charles had a duke or a count. What shall I tell you; for a single knight on the one side Charles could number thirty pennons. And the two hosts fell each upon the other with a tumult of battle cries, and with banners in array; and the stones and arrows flew from here and there, and knights were smitten down on every side.

For the space of three days the Lombards strove so valiantly that they slew a very great company of Charles's men. But on the third day Charles set in order the hardiest and bravest of his host and said to them—

"Go now, and win this battle, or return no more."

So King Didier together with the host of the Lombards fled to the place called Mortara, which was then known as Belle-Foret, because the country was so fair, there to refresh themselves and their horses. On the morning of the next day King Charles with his army drew near the town, and found the Lombards arrayed for the battle. So fierce was the combat that a great multitude of men were slain, both of one party and the other, and for reason of this slaying was the place named Mortara. There, too, on that field died Amis and Amile, for as it had pleased God to make their lives lovely and pleasant together, so in their deaths they were not divided. There also many another hardy knight was slain with the sword. But Didier, together with his Justiciary, and all the multitude of the Lombards, fled to Pavia; and King Charles followed closely after him and lay before the city, and invested it on every side; and lying there he sent to France to seek the Queen and his children. But St. Albin, the Bishop of Angers, and many another bishop and abbot counselled the King and Queen that they should bury those who fell in that battle, and build in that place a church. This counsel greatly pleased the King, so that on the field were built two churches, one by bidding of Charles in honour of St. Eusebius of Verceil, and the other by bidding of the Queen in honour of St. Peter.

Moreover the King caused to be brought the two coffins of stone wherein were buried Amis and Amile, and Amile was carried to the church of St. Peter, and Amis to the church of St. Eusebius. But on the morrow the body of Amile in his coffin of stone was found in the church of St. Eusebius near by the coffin of his comrade, Amis. So have you heard the story of this marvellous fellowship which could not be dissevered, even by death. This miracle did God for His servants —that God Who gave such power to His disciples that in His strength they might move even mountains. Because of this wonder the King and Queen tarried there for thirty days, giving fit burial to the bodies of the slain, and honouring those ministers with many rich gifts.

But all this while the host of Charles toiled mightily for the taking of the city before which it lay. Our Lord also tormented those within the walls so grievously that they might not bear their harness by reason of weakness and of death. At the end of ten months Charles took Didier the King, and all those who were with him, and possessed himself of the city and of all that realm. So Didier the King and his wife were led as captives into France.

But St. Albin, who in his day gave life to the dead and light to the blind, ordained clerks, and priests and deacons in the aforesaid church of St. Eusebius, and bade them always to hold in tireless keeping the bodies of those two comrades, Amis and Amile, who suffered death under Didier, King of Lombardy, the 12th day of October, and are now with our Lord Jesus Christ, Who liveth and reigneth with the Father and the Holy Ghost, world without end. Amen.

OF THE KNIGHT WHO PRAYED WHILST OUR LADY TOURNEYED IN HIS STEAD

SWEET Jesus, what brave warfare doth he make, and how nobly doth he joust, whose feet devoutly seek the church where the Divine Office is rendered, and who assists at the holy mysteries of Him, the spotless Son of the Mother Maid. For this cause will I tell you a certain story, even as it was told to me, for a fair ensample.

There was once a knight, esteemed of all as a wise and courteous lord, stout and of great valour, who dearly loved and honoured the Virgin Mary. The fame of this knight was bruited about all chivalry; so to make proof alike of lisping squire and burly man-at-arms, he set forth to a tourney, together with a strong company. Now by the will of God it chanced that when the day of the tournament was come he fared speedily towards the field, because he would be first at the breaking of the spears. Near by the road was builded a little church, and the bells thereof rang loud and clear to call men to the singing of the holy Mass. So without doubt or hesitation this knight dismounted at the door, and entered within the church to hearken to the service of God. At an altar therein a priest chanted meetly and with reverence a Mass of the holy Virgin Mary. Then another Mass was begun, the good knight yet kneeling devoutly on his knees, and praying our Lady with an earnest heart. When the second

Mass came to its appointed end, straightway a third
Mass was commenced, forthwith and in the selfsame
place.

"Sir, by the holy Body of God," said the squire to
his lord, "the hour to tourney hurries by. Why tarry
you here? Depart from hence, I pray you. Let us
keep to our own trade, lest men deem you hermit or
hyprocrite, or monk without the cowl!"

"Friend," answered the knight, "most worshipfully
doth he tourney who hearkens to the service of God
upon his knees. When the Masses are altogether at
an end, we will go upon our way. Till then, please
God, part from here will I not. But so that all are said,
then will I joust to the very utmost of my might, according to the will of God."

With these words the knight refrained from further
speech, and turning himself again towards the altar
took refuge in the holy liturgy, till the last prayer
came to a close with the last chant. Then they got to
horse, as was their bounden duty, and rode with speed
towards that place where the lists were set for the great
play. So, presently, the knights who were returning
from the tournament, discomfited and overborne, met
him who had carried off all the prizes of the game.
They saluted the knight who was on his way from the
Divine Offerings, and, joining themselves to his company, praised him to his face, affirming that never before had knight done such feats of arms as he had
wrought that day, to his undying fame. Moreover,
many amongst them drew near and yielded themselves
his captives, saying—

"We are your prisoners, for truly we may not deny
that you have overthrown us in the field."

Then, taking thought, the knight was amazed no
more, for quickly he perceived that She had been
upon his business in the press, about whose business
he had been within the chapel.

So he called these knights and his fellowship around
him, and said right courteously—

"I pray you, one and all, to hearken to my words,
for I have that to tell you which never has been heard
of ears."

Then he told over to them, word for word, how that
he had not jousted in the tournament, neither had
broken lance nor hung shield about his neck, by reason of those Masses he had heard, but verily he believed that the Maiden, whom humbly he had be-
sought within the chapel, had worn his harness in the
lists. "Altogether lovely in my eyes is this tournament
wherein She has done my devoir; but very foully shall
I requite such gracious service if I seek another Lady,
or in my folly return to the vanities of the world.
Therefore I pledge my word to God in truth, that
henceforth I will never fight, save in that tourney
where He sits, the one true Judge, Who knows the
loyal knight, and recompenses him according to his
deeds."

Then he bade them farewell right piteously, and
many of his company wept tenderly as they took their
leave. But he, parting from them, went his way to an
abbey, to become the servant of the Handmaid of the
Lord, and to follow in that path which leadeth to a
holy end.

So, clearly we may perceive from this ensample,
that the gracious God, in Whom we put our faith,
loves, cherishes, and delights to honour that man who

gladly tarries before His holy altar at the offering of the Mass, and who willingly serves His Mother, so gentle and so dear. Of much profit is this custom, and he who is quiet in the land and wise, will always continue to walk in the way his feet were set in youth, yea, even to that time when he is old and grey-headed.

THE PRIEST AND THE MULBERRIES

A CERTAIN priest having need to go to market, caused his mare to be saddled and brought to his door. The mare had carried her master for two years, and was high and well nourished, for during these years never had she known thirst nor hunger, but of hay and of oats ever had she enough and to spare. The priest climbed to the saddle and set out upon his journey, and well I remember that it was the month of September, for in that season mulberries grow upon the bushes in great plenty and abundance. The priest rode upon his way repeating his hours, his matins and his vigils. As he drew near the gate of the town the path ran through a certain deep hollow, and raising his eyes from his book the priest marked a bush thick with mulberries, bigger, blacker and more ripe than any he had ever seen. Desire entered his heart, for very covetous was he of this fair fruit, and gradually checking the pace of his mare, he presently caused her to stand beside the bush. Yet one thing still was wanting to his delight. The mulberries near the ground were set about with spines and thorns, whilst the sweetest of all hung so high upon the tree that in no wise could he reach them from his seat. This thing the priest saw, so in a while he climbed up, and stood with his two feet upon the saddle, whence by leaning over a little he could pluck the fruit. Then he chose the fairest, the ripest, and the sweetest of all these mulberries, eating them as swiftly and greedily

as he might, whilst the mare beneath him moved never
a whit. Now, when this priest had eaten as many mulberries as he was able, he glanced downwards, and
saw that the mare was standing still and coy, with her
head turned towards the bank of that deep road.
Thereat the priest rejoiced very greatly, for his two
feet were yet upon the saddle, and the mare was very
tall.

"God!" said he, "if any one now should cry 'Gee
up!'" He thought and spoke the words at the same
moment, whereat the mare was suddenly frighted, and
springing forward on the instant tumbled the luckless
priest into the bush where the thorns and briars grew
sharpest and thickest. There he lay in that uneasy bed,
nor might move from one side to the other, backwards
or forwards, for all the money in the mint.

The mare galloped straight to her own stable, but
when the priest's household saw her return in this
fashion they were greatly discomforted. The servants
cursed her for an evil and a luckless jade, whilst the
cook maid swooned like any dame, for well she believed that her master was dead. When they were returned a little to themselves they ran to and fro, here
and there, about the country searching for the priest,
and presently on their way to the market town they
drew near to that bush where their master yet lay in
much misease. On hearing their words bewailing his
piteous case, the priest raised a lamentable voice,
and cried—

"Diva, Diva, do not pass me by. This bush is an
uneasy bed, and here I lie very hurt and troubled
and utterly cast down. Do you not see how my blood
is staining these thorns and briars a vermeil red?"

The servants hurried to the bush, and stared upon the priest.

"Sir," said they, "who has flung you herein?"

"Alas," answered he, " 'tis sin that has undone me. This morning when I rode this way reading in my Book of Hours, I desired over greatly to eat of the mulberries growing hereon, and so I fell into the sin of gluttony. Therefore this bush gat hold upon me. But help me forth from this place, for I wish now for no other thing but to have a surgeon for my hurts, and to rest in my own house."

Now by this little story we may learn that the prudent man does not cry aloud all he may think in his heart, since by so doing many an one has suffered loss and shame, as we may see by this fable of the Priest and the Mulberries.

THE STORY OF ASENATH

IN the first of the seven years of great plenty Pharaoh sent forth Joseph to lay up corn, and gather food within the cities. So Joseph went out over all the land of Egypt, and came in the country of Heliopolis, where lived Poti-pherah, the priest, and chief counsellor of the great King. His daughter, Asenath, was the fairest of all the virgins of the earth; and seemed rather to be a daughter of Israel than an Egyptian. But Asenath was scornful and proud, and a despiser of men. No man of all the sons of men had seen her with his eyes, for she lodged within a strong tower, tall and wide, near by the habitation of Poti-pherah, the priest. Now high upon this tower were ten chambers. The first chamber was fair and great, and was builded of marble blocks of divers colours; the walls were of precious stones set in a chasing of gold, and the ceiling thereof was golden. There stood the gods of the Egyptians in metal of silver and gold, and Asenath bowed before them and offered sacrifice, every day of all the days. The second chamber was the habitation of Asenath, and was adorned cunningly with ornaments of gold and silver, with costly gems, and with arras and stuffs most precious. In the third chamber was brought together the wealth of all the world, and in that place also were set the aumbries of Asenath. Seven virgins, her fellows, lodged in the seven other chambers. They were very fair, and no man had spoken with them, nor any male child.

The chamber of Asenath was pierced with three windows; the first, which was very wide, looked towards the east, the second looked towards the south, and the third was set towards the north. Here was spread a couch of gold, covered with a purple coverlet, embroidered with golden thread, and hemmed with jacinths. There slept Asenath, with no bed-fellow, neither had man sat ever upon her bed. About this house was a goodly garden, closed round with a very strong wall, and entered by four iron gates. Each door had for warders eighteen men, very mighty and young, well armed and full of valour. At the right side of the garden sprang a fountain of living water, and near by the fountain a cistern which gave of this water to all the trees of the garden, and these trees bore much fruit. And Asenath was queenly as Sarah, gracious as Rebecca, and fair as Rachel.

How Joseph rebuked Asenath because she worshipped idols.

Joseph sent a message to Poti-pherah that he would come to his house. So Poti-pherah rejoiced greatly, saying to his daughter, "Joseph, the friend of God, enters herein. I would give thee to him as his wife."

But Asenath was sore vexed when she heard these words, and said—

"No captive shall ever be my husband, but only the son of a king."

Whilst they spake thus together, a messenger came before them and cried, "Joseph is here"; so Asenath fled to her chamber high within the tower. Now Joseph was seated in Pharaoh's own chariot of beaten gold, and it was drawn by four horses, white as snow, with bridles and harness of gold. Joseph was clad in a vesture of fine linen, white and glistering, and his mantle was of purple, spun with gold. He wore a golden circlet upon his head, and in this crown were set twelve stones, most precious, each stone having for ornament a golden star. Moreover, he held in his hand the royal sceptre, and an olive branch charged with fruit. Poti-pherah and his wife hastened to meet him, and bowed before him to the ground. They led him within the garden, and caused the doors to be shut. But when Asenath regarded Joseph from on high the tower, she repented her of the words she spoke concerning him, and said—

"Behold the sun and the chariot of the sun! Certainly this Joseph is the child of God; for what father could beget so fair an offspring, and what womb of woman could carry such light."

Joseph entered in the house of Poti-pherah, and whilst they washed his feet he asked what woman had looked forth from the window of the tower.

"Let her go forth from the house," he commanded.

This he said because he feared lest she should desire him, and should send him messages and divers gifts, even as other women of her nation, whom he had refused with holy indignation. But Poti-pherah replied—

"Sire, this is my daughter, who is a virgin, and hateth men; neither hath she seen any man save me, her father, and thyself this very day. If thou wilt, she shall come before thee and salute thee."

Then Joseph thought within himself, "Since she

hateth man, she will not cast her eyes upon me." So
he answered to her father—

"Since your daughter is a virgin, I will cherish her
even as my sister."

Then her mother went out to seek Asenath, and
brought her before Joseph.

"Salute thy brother," said Poti-pherah, "who hateth
the strange woman, even as thou hatest man."

"God keep thee," replied Asenath, "for thou art
blessed of God most high."

And Joseph answered, "May the God of life bless
thee evermore."

Then commanded Poti-pherah that she should kiss
Joseph; but as she drew near Joseph set his hand
against her breast and said—

"It is not meet that a man who worships the living
God, and eateth the bread of life and drinketh from
the chalice without corruption, should embrace the
strange woman, who bows down before deaf and dumb
idols; who serves them with the kisses of her mouth;
is anointed with their reprobate oil, and eats an accursed bread, and drinks unsanctified wine from their
table."

*Of the penitence of Asenath, and of the consolation
of an angel; how he came from Heaven to the chamber of Asenath, and spake with her and sweetly
comforted her.*

When Asenath heard Joseph speak these words she
was sore vexed, even unto tears; wherefore Joseph
took pity upon her and blessed her, laying his hand
upon her head. Asenath rejoiced greatly at the bene-
diction. She sought her bed, sick with fear and joy,

and renounced the gods before whom she bowed, and humbled herself to the ground. So Joseph ate and drank, and when he rose to go Poti-pherah prayed him to tarry till the morrow; but he might not, and parted, having promised to return within eight days.

Then Asenath put on sad raiment, such as she wore at the death of her brother, and went clothed in a garment of heaviness. She closed the doors of her chamber upon her and wept. Moreover, she flung forth all her idols by the window set towards the north; all the royal meat she gave to the dogs; she put dust upon her head, lay upon the ground, and lamented bitterly for seven days.

But the eighth morning, at the hour when the cock grows and the dogs howl at the breaking of the day, Asenath looked forth from the window giving to the east, and saw a star shining clear, and the heavens open, and there appeared a great light. She fell to earth with her face in the dust, and a man descended from the heavens and stood by her head, calling on her by her name. But Asenath answered nothing, because of the greatness of her fear. Then the man called her a second time, saying, "Asenath! Asenath!" and she replied—

"Lord, here am I. Tell me whom thou art."

And he said—

"I am Prince of the House of God and Captain of His Host. Rise, stand upon thy feet, for I have to speak with thee."

Then Asenath raised her head, and saw a man by her side who in all points was, as it were, Joseph. He was clad in a white stole, and bore the royal sceptre in his hand, and a crown was upon his brow. His face was as the lightning, his eyes as rays of the sun, and the hair of his head like a flame of fire. At the sight of him Asenath was sore afraid, and hid her face upon the ground. But the Angel raised her to her feet, and comforted her, saying—

"Put off this black raiment with which thou art clothed, and this girdle of sadness. Remove the sackcloth from thy body, and the dust from thine head; cleanse thy face and thy hands with living water, and adorn thee with fair apparel, for I have somewhat to say to thee."

So she adorned herself with speed, and when she came to him again he said—

"Asenath, take off this ornament from thine head, for thou art virgin. Rejoice, and be of good cheer, for thy name is written in the Book of Life, and shall never be taken away. Thou art born again this very day and quickened anew. For thou shalt receive the Bread of Blessing, and drink of the Wine without corruption; and be anointed with the Holy Chrism. Yea, I have given thee for wife to Joseph, and thou no more shall be called Asenath, but a name shall be given thee of fair refuge, for thy Penitence hath come before the High King, of whom she is the daughter, and thou shalt ever live before Him in mirth and gladness."

Then inquired she of the Angel his name, but he answered—

"My name is written by the finger of God in the Book of the most high King, but all that is written therein may not be told, neither is it proper for the hearing of mortal man."

Of the table and of the honey that Asenath set before the Angel, and how the Angel blessed Asenath.

But Asenath caught the Angel by his mantle, and said—

"If I have found favour in thine eyes, sit for a little space upon this bed, where never man has sat, and I will spread the table before my lord."

And the Angel replied, "Do quickly."

So Asenath set a fair linen cloth upon the table, and put thereon new bread of a sweet savour. Then said the Angel—

"Give me also a little honey in the honeycomb."

So Asenath was grievously troubled because she had no honey to set before her guest. But the Angel comforted her, saying—

"Look within thine aumbrey, and thou shalt find withal to furnish thy table."

Then she hastened thereto, and found a store of virgin honey, white as snow, of sweetest savour. So she spake to the Angel—

"Sire, I had no honey, but thou spakest the word, and it is there, and the perfume thereof is as the breath of thy mouth."

The Angel smiled at the understanding of Asenath, and placed his hand upon her head, and said—

"Blessed be thou, O Asenath, because thou hast forsaken thy idols, and believed in our living Lord. Yea, blessed are they whom Penitence bringeth before Him, for they shall eat of this honey gathered by the bees of Paradise from the dew of the roses of Heaven; and those who eat thereof shall never see death, but shall live for evermore."

Then the Angel stretched forth his hand and took of the honeycomb and break it; and he ate a little, and gave the rest to the mouth of Asenath, saying—

"This day hast thou eaten of the Bread of Life, and art anointed with the Holy Chrism. Beauty is given thee for ashes; for virtue shall never go from thee, neither shall thy youth wither, nor thy fairness fail; but thou shalt be as the strong city builded as a refuge for the children of our Lord, Who is King for ever more."

Then the Angel touched the honeycomb, and it became unbroken as before. Again he stretched forth his hand, and with his finger signed the cross thereon, and there where his finger touched came forth blood. So he spake to Asenath, and said—

"Behold this honey!"

Whilst she gazed thereon, she saw bees come forth from that honey, some white as snow, others vermeil as jacinths, and they gathered about her, and set virgin honey in the palm of her hand; and she ate thereof, and the Angel with her.

"Bees," said the Angel, "return now to your own place."

So they passed through that window which gave upon the east, and took their way to Paradise.

"Faithful as these bees are the words which I have spoken."

Then the Angel put forth his hand three times, and touched the honey, and fire came forth and consumed the honey without singeing the table, and the perfume which came from the honey and the fire was very sweet.

Of the blessing of the seven maidens, and of the marriage of Asenath, as set forth in the story.

Asenath said to the Angel—

"Lord, I have with me seven virgins, born in one

night, and nourished with me from my childhood until now. I will seek them, and thou shalt bless them, even as thou hast blessed me."

So she brought them before him, and he blessed them, saying—

"May the most high God bless you, and make you to be seven strong columns of the City of Refuge."

Afterwards he bade Asenath to carry forth the table, and whilst she went about her task, the Angel vanished from her eyes. But looking towards the east she saw, as it were, a chariot drawn by four horses ascending towards Heaven. So Asenath prayed to God right humbly that He would pardon the boldness with which she had spoken to the Captain of His Host.

Whilst she prayed thus a messenger came to Potipherah saying that Joseph, the friend of God, sought his house, and was even then at his door. Asenath hastened to meet him, and awaited his coming before the offices of the house. When Joseph entered the garden she bowed herself before him, and washed the dust from his feet, telling him the words which the Angel had spoken concerning her. The next day Joseph prayed Pharaoh that he might have Asenath to wife, and Pharaoh gave him the woman. He set also garlands of gold upon their heads, the fairest that cunning smiths could fashion, and caused them to embrace in the sight of men. So for seven days was kept high feast and festival, nor might any man labour for those days. He also gave them new names, calling Joseph, the Son of God, and Asenath, Daughter of the Most High King.

Before the time of the seven lean years Asenath bore two sons. And Joseph called the name of the first-born Manasseh, which is to say Forgetfulness; "For," said he, "God hath made me to forget all my toil, and all my father's house." And the name of the second was called Ephraim, which is to say Fruitfulness; "For," said he, "God hath caused me to be fruitful in the land of my affliction."

THE PALFREY

THAT men may bear in mind the fair deeds that woman has done, and to tell of her sweetness and frankness, this tale is here written. For very right it is that men should hold in remembrance the excellent virtues that can so easily be perceived in her. But grievous is it, and very heavy to me, that all the world does not laud and praise women to the height which is their due. Ah, God, if but they kept their hearts whole and unspotted, true and strong, the world would not contain so rich a treasure. The greater pity and sorrow, then, that they take not more heed to their ways, and that so little stay and stability are to be found in them. Too often the heart of a woman seems but a weathercock upon a steeple, whirled about in every wind that blows; so variable is woman's heart, and more changeable than any wind. But the story that I have taken upon me to narrate shall not remain untold because of the fickle-hearted, nor for reason of those who grudge praise to the frank and pure; therefore, give ear to this Lay of the Marvellous Palfrey.

Once upon a time a certain knight, courteous and chivalrous, rich of heart, but poor in substance, had his dwelling in the county of Champagne. So stout of heart was this lord, so wise in counsel, and so compact of honour and all high qualities, that had his fortune been equal to his deserts he would have had no peer amongst his fellows. He was the very pattern of the fair and perfect knight, and his praise was ever in the

mouth of men. In whatever land he came he was val-
ued at his proper worth, since strangers esteemed him
for the good that was told of him, and rumour but
increased his renown. When he had laced the helmet on his head, and ridden within the lists, he did
not court the glances of the dames, nor seek to joust
with those who were of less fame than he, but there
where the press was thickest he strove mightily in the
heart of the stour. In the very depths of winter he
rode upon his horse, attired in seemly fashion (since
in dress may be perceived the inclinations of the
heart) and this although his substance was but small.
For the lands of this knight brought him of wealth but
two hundred pounds of rent, and for this reason he
rode to tourneys in hope of gain as well as in quest of
honour.

This knight had set all his earthly hope and
thoughts on gaining the love of a certain noble lady.
The father of the damsel was a puissant Prince, lacking nought in the matter of wealth, and lord of a great
house furnished richly as his coffers. His fief and domain were fully worth one thousand pounds a year,
and many an one asked of him his fair daughter in
marriage, because her exceeding beauty was parcel of
the loveliness of the world. The Prince was old and
frail; he had no other child than the maiden, and his
wife had long been dead. His castle was builded in a
deep wood, and all about it stretched the great forest,
for in the days of my tale Champagne was a wilder
country then than now.

The gentle knight who had set his heart on the love
of the fair lady was named Messire William, and he
lived within the forest in an ancient manor some two

miles from the palace of the Prince. In their love they were as one, and ever they fondly dreamed one upon the other; but the Prince liked the matter but little, and had no mind that they should meet. So when the knight would gaze upon the face of his mistress, he went secretly by a path that he had worn through the profound forest, and which was known of none save him. By this path he rode privily on his palfrey, without gossip or noise, to visit the maiden, many a time. Yet never might these lovers see each other close, however great was their desire, for the wall of the courtyard was very high, and the damsel was not so hardy as to issue forth by the postern. So for their solace they spoke together through a little gap in the wall, but ever between them was the deep and perilous fosse, set thickly about with hedges of thorn and spine, so that never closer might they meet. The castle of the Prince was builded upon a high place, and was strongly held with battlement and tower; moreover, bridge and portcullis kept his door. The ancient knight, worn by years and warfare, seldom left his lodging, for he might no longer get him to horse. He lived within his own house, and ever would have his daughter seated at his side, to cheer his lonely age with youth. Often this thing was grievous to her, for she failed to come to that fair spot where her heart had taken root. But the brave knight in nowise forgot the road that he had worn, and asked for nothing more than to see her somewhat closer with his eyes.

Now the tale tells that in spite of his poverty the knight owned one thing that was marvellously rich. The palfrey on which he rode had not his like in all the world. It was grey and of a wonderful fair colour,

so that no flower was so bright in semblance, nor did
any man know of so beautiful a steed. Be assured that
not in any kingdom could be discovered so speedy a
horse, nor one that carried his rider so softly and so
surely. The knight loved his palfrey very dearly, and
I tell you truly that in nowise would he part with him
for any manner of wealth, though the rich folk of that
country, and even from afar, had coveted him for
long. Upon this fair palfrey Messire William went often to his lady, along the beaten path through the
solitary forest, known but to these two alone. Right
careful was he to keep this matter from the father of
the demoiselle; and thus, though these two lovers had
such desire one of the other, they might not clasp their
arms about the neck, nor kiss, nor embrace, nor for
their solace, even, hold each other by the hand.
Nought could they do but speak, and hearken softly
to such sweet words, for well they knew that should
the old Prince know thereof, very swiftly would he
marry his daughter to some rich lord.

Now the knight considered these things within himself, and day by day called to remembrance the
wretched life that was his, for he might not put the
matter from his mind. So at the end he summoned all
his courage, and for weal or woe resolved that he
would go to the aged Prince and require of him his
daughter for his wife, let that betide what may. For
very clear it was to him that such a life he could not
lead for every day of the week. On a certain day he
made himself ready, and repaired to the castle where
the demoiselle dwelt with her father. He was welcomed very gladly by the Prince and his company, for
he was esteemed a courteous and gentle knight, and

bragged of by all men as a valiant gentleman, who was lacking in no good qualities.

"Sire," said the knight, "I ask you of your grace to listen to my words. I enter in your house to crave of you such a gift as may God put it in your heart to bestow."

The old man looked upon him fixedly, and afterwards inquired—

"What is it you would have? Tell me now, for by my faith I will aid you if I may, yet in all things saving my honour."

"Yea, sire, very easily you may do this thing, if so you please. May God but grant that such is your pleasure."

"I will grant you the gift if it seems to me well, and I will refuse you the boon if it seems to me ill. Nothing will you get from me, neither gift, nor promise, nor blame, that it is not fitting for me to bestow."

"Sire," answered he, "I will tell you the gift I crave at your hand. You know who I am, and right well you knew my father. Well, too, you know my manor and my household, and all those things wherein I take my pleasure and delight. In guerdon of my love, I pray—so it may please you, sire—your daughter as my wife. God grant that my prayer may not disturb your heart, and that my petition may not be refused to my shame. For I will not hide from you that although I am not of her fellowship, yet have I spoken from afar with my demoiselle, and perceived those fair virtues which all men praise. Greatly is my lady loved and esteemed in these parts, for truly there is not her like in all the world. I have been too rash, since I have dared to require so gracious a gift, but so you deign to give to my asking, joyous and merry shall I go for all my days. Now have I told you my petition; so answer me according to my hope and your good pleasure."

The old man had no need for counsel in this matter, so without delay he made answer to the knight—

"I have heard with patience what you had to tell. Certes, and without doubt, my daughter is fair, and fresh, and pure, and a maiden of high descent. For myself, I am a rich vavasour, and come of noble ancestry, having fief and land worth fully one thousand pounds each year in rent. Think you I am so besotted as to give my daughter to a knight who lives by play! I have no child but one, who is close and dear to my heart, and after I am gone all my wealth will be hers. She shall wed no naked man, but in her own degree; for I know not any prince of this realm, from here even to Lorraine, however wise and brave, of whom she would not be more than worthy. It is not yet a month agone since such a lord as this prayed her at my hand. His lands were worth five hundred pounds in rent, and right willingly would he have yielded them to me, had I but hearkened to his suit. But my daughter can well afford to wait, for I am so rich that she may not easily lose her price, nor miss the sacrament of marriage. Too high is this fruit for your seeking, for there is none in this realm, nor from here to Allemaigne, however high his race, who shall have her, save he be count or king."

The knight was all abashed at these proud words. He did not wait for further shame, but took his leave, and went as speedily as he might. But he knew not what to do, for Love, his guide, afflicted him very grievously, and bitterly he complained him thereof. When the maiden heard of this refusal, and was told the despiteful words her father had spoken, she was grieved in her very heart, for her love was no girl's light fancy, but was wholly given to the knight, far more than any one can tell. So when the knight—yet heavy and wrathful—came to the accustomed trysting place to speak a little to the maiden, each said to the other what was in the mind. There he opened out to her the news of his access to her father, and of the disaccord between the twain.

"Sweet my demoiselle," said the knight, "what is there to do? It seems better to me to quit my home, and to dwell henceforth amongst strangers in a far land, for my last hope is gone. I may never be yours, neither know I how these things will end. Cursed be the great wealth with which your father is so puffed up. Better had it been that you were not so rich a dame, for he would have looked upon my poverty with kinder eyes if his substance were not so great."

"Certes," answered she, "very gladly would I be no heiress, but only simple maid, if all things were according to my will. Sire, if my father took heed only to your good qualities, by my faith he would not pain himself to prevent your coming to me. If he but weighed your little riches in the balance against your great prowess, right soon would he conclude the bargain. But his heart cannot be moved: he does not wish what I would have, nor lament because I may wring my hands. If he accorded with my desire, right speedily would this matter be ended. But age and youth walk not easily together, for in the heart is the difference between the old and young. Yet so you do ac-

cording to my device, you shall not fail to gain what
you would have."

"Yea, demoiselle, by my faith, I will not fail herein; so tell me now your will."

"I have determined on a thing to which I have
given thought many a time and oft. Very surely you
remember that you have an uncle who is right rich in
houses and in goods. He is not less rich than my father; he has neither child, wife nor brother, nor any
kindred of his blood nearer than you. Well is it known
that all his wealth is yours when he is dead, and this
in treasure and in rent is worth sixty marks of virgin
gold. Now go to him without delay, for he is old and
frail; tell him that between my father and yourself is
such a business that it may not come to a good end
unless he help therein. But that if he would promise
you three hundred pounds of his land, and come to
require grace of my father, very soon can the affair be
ended. For my father loves him dearly, and each
counts the other an honourable man. Your uncle
holds my father as prudent and wise: they are two
ancient gentlemen, of ripe years, and have faith and
affiance the one in the other. Now if for love of you
your uncle would fairly seek my father and speak him
thus, 'I will deliver to my nephew three hundred
pounds of my lands, so that you give him your child,'
why, the marriage will be made. I verily believe that
my father would grant your uncle his request, if only
he would ask me of him. And when we are wedded together, then you can render again to your uncle all
the land that he has granted you. And so sweetly do
I desire your love, that right pleasing I shall find the
bargain."

"Fairest," cried the knight, "verily and truly there is nothing I crave in comparison with your love; so forthwith I will find my uncle, and tell him this thing."

The knight bade farewell, and went his way, yet thoughtful and bewildered and sad, by reason of the shame which had been put upon him. He rode at adventure through the thick forest upon his grey palfrey. But as he rode fear left him, and peace entered in his heart, because of the honest and wise counsel given him by the fair maiden. He came without hindrance to Medet, where his uncle had his dwelling, but when he was entered into the house he bewailed his lot, and showed himself all discomforted. So his uncle took him apart into a privy chamber, and there he opened out his heart, and made plain to him all this business.

"Uncle," said he, "if you will do so much as to speak to her sire, and tell him that you have granted me three hundred pounds of your land, I will make this covenant with you, and plight you my faith, my hand in yours, that when I have wedded her who is now denied me, that I will render again and give you quittance for your land. Now I pray that you will do what is required of you."

"Nephew," answered the uncle, "this I will do willingly, since it pleases me right well. By my head, married you shall be, and to the pearl of all the country, for good hope have I to bring this matter to an end."

"Uncle," said the knight, "put your hand to my task, and so press on with the business that time may go swiftly to the wedding. For my part I will arm me richly, and ride to the tournament at Galardon, where, by the aid of God, I trust to gain such ransom

as will be helpful to me. And I pray you to use such
diligence that I may be married on my return."

"Fair nephew, right gladly," answered he, "for
greatly it delights me that so gracious and tender a
lady shall be your bride."

So without further tarrying Messire William went
his way, merry of heart because of his uncle's promise
that without let he should have as wife that maid
whom so dearly he desired. For of other happiness he
took no heed. Thus blithe and gay of visage he rendered him to the tournament, as one who had no care
in all the world.

On the morrow, very early in the morning, the uncle got to horse, and before the hour of prime came to
the rich mansion of that old Prince, and of her whose
beauty had no peer. He was welcomed with high observance, for the ancient lord loved him very dearly,
seeing that they were both of the same years, and were
rich and puissant princes, near neighbours in that
land. Therefore he rejoiced greatly that one so high
in station did honour to his house, and spread before
him a fair banquet, with many sweet words, for the
old Prince was frank and courteous of heart, and knew
to praise meetly where honour was due. When the tables were cleared, the two spake together of old faces
and old stories, shields, and swords and spears, and of
many a doughty deed, in the most loving fashion. But
the uncle of the good knight would not forget his
secret thought, and presently discovered it to the
Prince in saying—

"What go I now to tell you? I love you very truly,
as you may easily perceive. I am come to require a
favour at your hand. May God put it into your heart

to lend your ear to my prayer in such a fashion that
the matter may be brought to a right fair end."

"By my head," answered the old Prince, "you are so
near to my heart that you are not likely to be refused
aught that you may ask of me. Tell me, that I may
grace you with the gift."

"Sire, thanks and thanks again, for I would do the
same by you," returned the uncle of the knight, who
no longer cared to hide his privy mind. "I am come
to pray of you, fair sire, the hand of your virtuous
maid in marriage. When we once were wed I would
endow her with my wealth to the utmost of my power.
You know well that I have no heir of my body,
which troubles me sorely; and I will keep good faith
with you herein, for I am he who loves you dearly.
When your daughter is bestowed upon me, it would
not be my care to separate father and child, nor to
withdraw my wealth from yours, but all our substance
should be as one, and we would enjoy together in
common that which God has given us."

When he whose heart was crafty heard these words,
he rejoiced greatly, and made reply—

"Sire, I will give her to you right gladly, for you are
a loyal and an honourable man. I am more content
that you have required her of me than if the strongest
castle of these parts had been rendered to my hand.
To none other in the world would I grant my maid so
willingly as to you, for you are prudent and hardy,
and many a time have I proved ere now that I may
have confidence in your faith."

Then was promised and betrothed the damsel to a
husband of whom she had little envy, for she was persuaded that another had asked her as his wife. When

the maiden knew the truth thereof she was altogether amazed and sorrowful, and often she swore by St. Mary that never should she be wedded of him. Right heavy was she, and full of tears, and grievously she lamented her fate.

"Alas, unhappy wretch, for now I am dead. What foul treason has this old traitor done, for which he justly should be slain! How shamefully he has deceived that brave and courteous knight, whose honour is untouched by spot. By his wealth this aged, ancient man has bought me at a price. May God requite it to his bosom, for he purposes to commit a great folly, since the day we are wed he takes his mortal foe to wife. How may I endure that day! Alas, may God grant that I shall never see that hour, for too great is the anguish that I suffer because of this treason. If I were not fast in prison, right swiftly would I get quit of this trouble, but nought is there for me to do, since in no wise can I flee from this manor. So stay I must, and suffer as my father wills, but truly my pain is more than I can bear. Ah, God, what will become of me, and when shall he return who so foully is betrayed. If he but knew the trick his uncle has set on him, and how, too, I am taken in the snare, well I know that he would die of grief. Ah, if he but knew! Sure I am that he would ride with speed, and that soon these great woes would be as they had never been. Too sorely is my heart charged with sorrow, and better I love to die than to live. Alas, that this old man ever should cast his thought upon me, but none may deliver me now, for my father loves him because of his wealth. Fie on age! Fie upon riches! Never may bachelor wed with loving maid save he have money in his pouch.

Cursed be the wealth which keeps me from him wherein I have my part, for truly my feet are caught in a golden net."

In this wise the maiden bewailed her lot, by reason of her great misease. For so sweetly was her heart knit in the love of her fair bachelor, that in nowise might she withdraw her thoughts from him. Therefore she held in the more despite him to whom her father had given her. Old he was, very aged, with a wrinkled face, and red and peering eyes. From Chalons to Beauvais there was no more ancient knight than he, nor from there to Sens a lord more rich, for that matter. But all the world held him as pitiless and felon; whilst so beautiful and brave was the lady, that men knew no fairer heiress, nor so courteous and simple a maiden, no, not within the Crown of France. How diverse were these twain. On one side was light, and on the other darkness; but there was no spot in the brightness, and no ray within the dark. But the less grief had been hers had she not set her love on so perilous a choice.

Now he to whom the damsel was betrothed, because of his exceeding content, made haste to appoint some near day for the wedding. For he knew little that she was as one distraught by reason of the great love she bore his nephew, as you have heard tell. So her father made all things ready, very richly, and when the third day was come he sent letters to the greybeards, and to those he deemed the wisest of that land, bidding them to the marriage of his daughter, who had bestowed her heart elsewhere. Since he was well known to all the country round, a great company of his friends came together to the number of thirty, to do honour to his house, since not one of them but owed him service for his lands. Then it was accorded between them that the demoiselle should be wedded early on the morrow, and her maidens were bidden to prepare their lady for the wedding on the appointed day and hour. But very wrathful and troubled in heart were the maidens by reason of this thing.

The Prince inquired of the damsels if his daughter was fitly arrayed against her marriage, and had content therein, or was in need of aught that it became her state to have.

"Nothing she needs, fair sire," made answer one of her maidens, "so far as we can see; at least so that we have palfreys and saddles enow to carry us to the church, for of kinsfolk and of cousins are a many near this house."

"Do not concern yourself with the palfreys," replied the Prince, "for I trow we shall have to spare. There is not a lord bidden to the wedding whom I have not asked to lend us from his stables."

Then, making no further tarrying, he returned to his own lodging, with peace and confidence in his heart.

Messire William, that brave and prudent knight, had little thought that his marriage was drawing so near its term. But Love held him so fast that he made haste to return, for ever the remembrance of her face was before his eyes. Since love flowered so sweetly within his heart, he parted from the tournament in much content, for he deemed that he rode to receive the gift he desired beyond all the world. Such he hoped was the will of God, and such the end of the adventure. Therefore he awaited in his manor, with what patience he might, the fair and pleasant tidings his uncle must presently send him, to hasten to the spousal of his bride. Since he had borne off all the prizes of the tourney, he bade a minstrel to his hall, and sang joyously to the playing of the viol. Yet, though all was revelry and merriment, often he looked towards the door to see one enter therein with news. Much he marvelled when the hour would bring these welcome words, and often he forgot to mark the newest refrains of the minstrel, because his thoughts were otherwhere. At the time hope was growing sick a varlet came into the courtyard. When Messire William saw him the heart in his breast leaped and fluttered for joy.

"Sire," said the varlet, "God save you. My lord, your friend, whom well you know, has sent me to you in his need. You have a fair palfrey, than which none goes more softly in the world. My lord prays and requires of you that for love of him you will lend him this palfrey, and send it by my hand forthwith."

"Friend," answered the knight, "for what business?"

"Sire, to carry his lady daughter to the church, who is so dainty-sweet and fair."

"For what purpose rides she to church?"

"Fair sire, there to marry your uncle to whom she is betrothed. Early to-morrow morn my lady will be brought to the ancient chapel deep within the forest. Hasten, sire, for already I tarry too long. Lend your palfrey to your uncle and my lord. Well we know that it is the noblest horse within the realm, as many a time has been proved."

When Messire William heard these words—

"God," said he, "then I am betrayed by him in whom I put my trust; to whom I prayed so much to help me to my hope. May the Lord God assoil him never for his treasonable deed. Yet scarcely can I believe that he has done this wrong. It is easier to hold that you are telling me lies."

"Well, you will find it truth to-morrow at the ringing of prime; for already is gathered together a company of the ancient lords of these parts."

"Alas," said he, "how, then, am I betrayed and tricked and deceived."

For a very little Messire William would have fallen swooning to the earth, had he not feared the blame of his household. But he was so filled with rage and grief that he knew not what to do, nor what to say. He did not cease lamenting his evil case till the varlet prayed him to control his wrath.

"Sire, cause the saddle to be set forthwith on your good palfrey, so that my lady may be carried softly to the church."

Then Messire William considered within himself to know whether he should send his grey palfrey to him whom he had cause to hate more than any man.

"Yea, without delay," said he, "since she who is the soul of honour has nothing to do with my trouble. My palfrey shall bear her gladly, in recompense of the favours she has granted me, for naught but kindness have I received of her. Never shall I have of her courtesies again, and all my joy and happiness are past. Now must I lend my palfrey to the man who has betrayed me to my death, since he has robbed me of that which I desired more than all the world. No man is bound to return love for treason. Very rash is he to require my palfrey of me, when he scrupled not to take the sweetness, the beauty and the courtesy with which my demoiselle is endowed. Alas, now have I served her in vain, and my long hope is altogether gone. No joy in my life is left, save to send her that thing which it breaks my heart to give. Nevertheless, come what may, my palfrey shall go to the most tender of maidens. Well I know that when she sets her eyes upon him she will bethink her of me; of me and of my love, for I love and must love her all the days of my life, yea, though she has given her heart to those who have wounded mine. But sure am I that this thing is not seemly to her, for Cain, who was brother to Abel, wrought no fouler treason."

In this manner the knight bewailed his heavy sorrow. Then he caused a saddle to be set upon the palfrey, and calling the servitor delivered the horse to his keeping. So the varlet forthwith went upon his way.

Messire William, yet heavy and wrathful, shut himself fast within his chamber to brood upon his grief. He charged his household that if there was a man so bold as to seek to hearten him in his sorrow he would cause him to be hanged. For his part he had no care for mirth, and would live withdrawn from men, since he might never lose the pain and sorrow that weighed upon his heart.

But whilst the knight was in this case, the servant in custody of the palfrey returned with all the speed he might to the castle of the old Prince, where all was merriment and noise.

The night was still and serene, and the house was filled with a great company of ancient lords. When they had eaten their full, the Prince commanded the watch that, without fail, all men should be roused and apparelled before the breaking of the day. He

bade, too, that the palfrey and the horses should be
saddled and made ready at the same hour, without
confusion or disarray. Then they went to repose themselves and sleep. But one amongst them had no hope
to sleep, because of the great unrest she suffered by
reason of her love. All the night she could not close
her eyes. Others might rest: she alone remained awake,
for her heart knew no repose.

Now shortly after midnight the moon rose very
bright, and shone clearly in the heavens. When the
warder saw this thing, being yet giddy with the wine
that he had drunken, he deemed that the dawn had
broken.

"Pest take it," said he, "the lords should be about
already."

He sounded his horn and summoned and cried—
"Arouse you, lords, for day is here."

Then those, yet drowsy with sleep, and heavy with
last night's wine, got them from their beds all bewildered. The squires, too, made haste to set saddles upon
the horses, believing that daybreak had come, though
before the dawn would rise very easily might the
horses go five miles, ambling right pleasantly. So when
the company which should bring this demoiselle to
the chapel deep within the forest were got to horse,
her father commended his maid to the most trusty of
his friends. Then the saddle was put upon the grey
palfrey; but when it was brought before the damsel
her tears ran faster than they had fallen before. Her
guardian recked nothing of her weeping, for he knew
little of maidens, and considered that she wept because of leaving her father and her father's house. So
her tears and sadness were accounted as nought, and

she mounted upon her steed, making great sorrow. They took their way through the forest, but the road was so narrow that two could not ride together side by side. Therefore the guardian put the maiden before, and he followed after, because of the straitness of the path. The road was long, and the company were tired and weary for want of sleep. They rode the more heavily, because they were no longer young, and had the greater need for rest. They nodded above the necks of their chargers, and up hill and down dale for the most part went sleeping. The surest of this company was in charge of the maiden, but this night he had taken so little sleep in his bed that he proved an untrusty warder, for he forgot everything, save his desire to sleep. The maiden rode, bridle in hand, thinking of nought except her love and her sorrow. Whilst she followed the narrow path the barons who went before had already come forth upon the high road. They dozed in their saddles, and the thoughts of those few who were awake were otherwhere, and gave no heed to the demoiselle. The maiden was as much alone as though she fared to London. The grey palfrey knew well this ancient narrow way, for many a time he had trodden it before. The palfrey and the maiden drew near a hillock within the forest, where the trees stood so close and thick that no moonlight fell within the shadow of the branches. The valley lay deeply below, and from the high road came the noise of the horses' iron shoes. Of all that company many slept, and those who were awake talked together, but none gave a thought to the maiden. The grey palfrey knew nothing of the high road, so turning to the right he entered within a little path, which led directly to the house of Messire William. But the knight, in whose charge the damsel was placed had fallen into so heavy a slumber that his horse stood at his pleasure on the way. Therefore she was guarded of none—save of God—and dropping the rein upon the palfrey's neck, she let him have his will. The knights who preceded her rode a great while before they found that she was not behind them, and he who came after kept but a poor watch and ward. Nevertheless she had not escaped by her choice, for she recked nought of the path that she followed, nor of the home to which she would come. The palfrey followed the track without hesitation, for many a time he had journeyed therein, both winter and summer. The weeping maiden looked this way and that, but could see neither knight nor baron, and the forest was very perilous, and all was dark and obscure. Much she marvelled what had become of all her company, and it was no wonder that she felt great fear. None regarded her safety, save God and the grey palfrey, so she commended herself to her Maker, whilst the horse ambled along the road. Nevertheless she had dropped the rein from her fingers, and kept her lips from uttering one single cry, lest she should be heard of her companions. For she chose rather to die in the woodlands than to endure such a marriage as this. The maiden was hid in thought, and the palfrey, in haste to reach his journey's end, and knowing well the path, ambled so swiftly, that soon he came to the borders of the forest. A river ran there both dark and deep, but the horse went directly to the ford, and passed through as quickly as he was able. He had won but little beyond when the maiden heard the sound of a horn, blown from that place where she was carried by the grey palfrey. The warder on his tower blew shrilly on his horn, and the demoiselle felt herself utterly undone, since she knew not where she had come, nor how to ask her way. But the palfrey stayed his steps on a bridge which led over the moat running round the manor. When the watch heard the noise of the palfrey thereon, he ceased his winding, and coming from the tower demanded who it was who rode so hardily on the bridge at such an hour. Then the demoiselle made reply—

"Certes, it is the most unlucky maid of mother born. For the love of God give me leave to enter in your house to await the day, for I know not where to go."

"Demoiselle," answered he, "I dare not let you or any other in this place, save at the bidding of my lord, and he is the most dolorous knight in all the world, for very foully has he been betrayed."

Whilst the watch spoke of the matter he set his eye to a chink in the postern. He had neither torch nor lantern, but the moon shone very clear, and he spied the grey palfrey, which he knew right well. Much he marvelled whence he came, and long he gazed upon the fair lady who held the rein, and was so sweetly clad in her rich new garnishing. Forthwith he sought his lord, who tossed upon his bed with little delight.

"Sire," said he, "be not wrath with me. A piteous woman, tender of years and semblance, has come forth from the woodland, attired right richly. It seems to me that she is cloaked in a scarlet mantle, edged with costly fur. This sad and outworn lady is mounted on your own grey palfrey. Very enticing is her speech; very slim and gracious is her person. I know not, sire, if I am deceived, but I believe there is no maiden in all

the country who is so dainty, sweet and fair. Well I
deem that it is some fay whom God sends you, to bear
away the trouble which is spoiling your life. Take now
the gold in place of the silver you have lost."

Messire William hearkened to these words. He
sprang forth from his bed without further speech, and
with nothing but a surcoat on his back hastened to
the door. He caused it to be opened forthwith, and
the demoiselle cried to him pitifully in a loud voice—

"Woe is me, gentle lord, because of the sorrow I
have endured this night. Sire, for the love of God turn
me not away, but suffer me to enter in your house. I
beg for shelter but a little while. But much I fear by
reason of a company of knights who are pained greatly, since they have let me from their hands. Sir Knight,
be surety for the maid whom Fortune has guided to
your door, for much am I sorrowful and perplexed."

When Messire William heard her voice he was like
to swoon with joy. He knew again the palfrey which
was so long his own. He gazed upon the lady, and
knew her in his heart. I tell you truly that never could
man be more happy than was he. He lifted her from
the palfrey and brought her within his home. There he
took her by the right hand, kissing her more than
twenty times; and for her part the lady let him have
his way, because she had looked upon his face. When
the two sought each other's eyes, very great was the
joy that fell between the twain and all their sorrow
was as if it had never been. So when the damsel had
put aside her mantle, they seated themselves merrily
on silken cushions, fringed with gold. They crossed
their brows again and yet again, lest they should wake

and find this thing a dream. Then the maiden told
her bachelor this strange adventure, and said—

"Blessed be the hour in which God brought me to
this place, and delivered me from him who sought to
add my marriage chest to his own coffers."

When morning was come Messire William arrayed
himself richly, and led the demoiselle within the chapel of his own house. Then, without delay, he called
his chaplain to him, and was forthwith wedded to the
fair lady by a rite that it was not lawful to call in
question. So when the Mass was sung, blithe was the
mirth of that household, squire and maiden and man-
at-arms.

Now when that company which so lightly had lost
the maiden came together at the ancient chapel, they
were very weary by having ridden all the night, and
were sore vexed and utterly cast down. The old Prince
demanded his daughter of him who had proved so
untrusty a guardian. Knowing not what to say, he
made answer straightly—

"Sire, because of the strictness of the way I put the
maid before, and I followed after. The forest was deep
and dark, and I know not where she turned from the
path. Moreover, I nodded in my saddle till I was waked
by my companions, for I deemed that she was yet in
my company, but she was altogether gone. I cannot
tell what has become of the damsel, for very basely
have we kept our trust."

The old Prince sought his daughter in every place,
and inquired of her from every person, but he might
not find her whereabouts, nor hear of any who had
seen the maid. Yet all men marvelled at her loss, for

none was able to bring him any news. The ancient bridegroom, that the demoiselle should have wed, grieved yet more at the loss of his bride, but to no purpose did he seek her, for the hind had left no slot. Now as the two lords were riding with their company in such fear as this, they saw upon the road a certain squire making towards them in all haste. When he was come to them he said—

"Sire, Messire William sends by me assurance of the great friendship he bears you. He bids me say that early this morning, at the dawn of day, he married your daughter, to his great happiness and content. Sire, he bids you welcome to his house. He also charged me to say to his uncle, who betrayed him so shamefully, that he pardons him the more easily for his treason, since your daughter has given him herself as a gift."

The old Prince hearkened to this wonder, but said no word in reply. He called together all his barons, and when they were assembled in hall, he took counsel as to whether he should go to the house of Sir William, and bring with him the lord to whom his daughter was betrothed. Yet since the marriage was done, nothing could make the bride again a maid. So, making the best of a bad bargain, he got to horse forthwith, and all his barons with him. When the company came to the manor they were welcomed with all fair observance, for right pleasing was this to Messire William, since he had all things to his own desire. Whether he would, or whether he would not, nought remained to the old Prince but to embrace his son-in-law; whilst as to that greybeard of a bridegroom, he consoled himself with what crumbs of comfort he could discover. Thus, since it was the will of God that these lovers should be wed, it pleased the Lord God also that the marriage should prove lasting.

Messire William, that courteous and chivalrous knight, lost not his hardihood in marriage, but ever sought advancement, so that he was esteemed of the counts and princes of his land. In the third year of his marriage the old Prince (as the tale tells us) died, because his time was come. So all that he died possessed of in wealth and lands and manors, together with the rich garnishing thereof, became the heritage of the knight. After this, Death laid hands upon his uncle, who, too, was very rich. And Sir William, who was not simple, nor grudging of heart, nor little of soul, nor blusterous with his neighbours, inherited all the goods that were his.

So the story which I have told you endeth in this fashion, in accordance with the truth, and to your pleasure.